THINKERS OF OUR TIME

POLANYI

THINKERS OF OUR TIME

POLANYI

Richard Allen

The Claridge Press
London

First published in Great Britain 1990

by The Claridge Press
6 Linden Gardens
London W2 4ES
and Box 420
Lexington
Georgia 30648

Copyright © Richard Allen

Typeset by
Fingerprint Graphics
London N1
and printed by
Short Run Press
Exeter, Devon

ISBN 1-870626-51-6 (Hardback)
ISBN 1-870626-56-7 (Paperback)

Allen, Richard: *Polanyi*

1. Political Science

CONTENTS

ABBREVIATIONS

All references to Polanyi's works will be given in the text using the following abbreviations:

KB — *Knowing and Being*
LL — *The Logic of Liberty*
PK — *Personal Knowledge*
SOM — *The Study of Man*
SFS — *Science, Faith and Society,* 2nd ed.
TD — *The Tacit Dimension*

Also:

WH — E. Wigner and R. Hodgkin, 'Michael Polanyi', *Biographical Memoirs of Fellows of the Royal Society*, Vol. 23, Dec. 1977.

1. THE EMERGENCE OF THE PHILOSOPHER

It has been the fate of Michael Polanyi, like that of A.N. Whitehead and R.G. Collingwood, to have become better known and appreciated in North America than in Britain, despite the fact that Polanyi made England his home in 1933. Perhaps that is because he was, like Whitehead and Collingwood, a man of wide interests, and outside the schools of analytic and linguistic philosophy which predominated in Britain at the time when Polanyi turned to philosophy, and published *Personal Knowledge* in 1958.

Moreover he was not a professional philosopher. He came to philosophy in the middle of a very distinguished career in physical chemistry, at which he was also an amateur. Now academic philosophers are usually concerned with the technical problems bequeathed them by their predecessors. Either they seek to develop the type of philosophy which they have been taught, or they react against what they perceive to be its errors. Not so Polanyi. He found himself taking up philosophy because of his desire to protect the freedom of science against Marxist schemes to subordinate it to technology, central control and the general welfare. He found current thinking about science and freedom inadequate. He was then led into thinking and writing about the wider political and economic freedoms upon which the freedom of science rests, and then upon the fundamental issues of truth, belief, authority and conscience. In his principal work, *Personal Knowledge,* he sought to change the whole way of thinking about such issues. His target was 'Objectivism', the assumption that knowledge must be a function of the observed object alone, and that any personal shaping of his knowledge by the knower renders it 'merely subjective'. He sought to show that knowledge is and must be a personal achievement. He argued his case by reference to the ground where those of an Objectivist outlook usually take their stand — physics and chemistry, the exact sciences which they believe to embody their ideal of a precise, detached and impersonal knowledge. But most philosophers thirty years ago were not ready, either for a philosophy which had something positive to say, or for the radical shift of outlook which Polanyi was endeavouring to bring about.

Yet it is most appropriate that a volume on Polanyi should appear in a series devoted to Thinkers of our Time. For he sought to liberate us from the dangerous errors that have infected modern thought since Galileo and Descartes: the quest for assured knowledge through the method of doubting everything that we claim to know; the Scepticism to which this eventually leads, with regard to everything that is not known by pure observation and exact and impersonal measurement; the Reductionism that sees Nature, and eventually man himself, as merely a mechanical system of matter in motion, to be studied by the methods of physics and chemistry; the manipulative attitude to others that results from the Reductionist view of mankind; the Nihilism that results from the method of doubt and the consequent critical corrosion of established beliefs, and finally of the power to believe; and then, with the secularisation of Christian eschatology, the highly dangerous combination of Scepticism with a secularised eschatology, which has resulted in the totalitarian ideologies, world war, death or slavery for millions, and the contemporary scourge of terrorism. It is issues such as these which concerned Polanyi and which led him to formulate a 'post-critical philosophy' (the sub-title to *Personal Knowledge*) as an answer to the intellectual causes of our present discontents. His thinking and his work deserve to be more widely known, especially now that philosophy has fully escaped from the cramps and limitations of conceptual analysis and is open again to the study of real problems.

Michael Polanyi was born in Budapest on March 11th, 1891, into a well-to-do family of Jewish origin. He had two brothers and two sisters, all older than himself. His father, a civil engineer and entrepreneur, lost his money in 1899 and died in 1905, but his mother continued to run a *salon* for poets, painters and scholars. In marked contrast to others in his circle, he was always sceptical of socialism. And 'in a flock of black sheep he seemed almost white .... What made him differ most from those around him was his reverence' (P. Ignotus, p.12). Those who knew him speak of him always as a gentle person of quiet authority.

In 1909 he entered the University of Budapest to read medicine, but soon became inclined to research, and, at the age of 19, published his first paper, 'Chemistry of the hydrocephalic liquid'. Two years later he wrote a paper on the Third Law of Thermodynamics, which gained Einstein's commendation. He graduated in 1913 and went to the Technische Hochschule in Karlsruhe to study chemistry, but returned in 1914 to serve as a medical officer in the Austro-Hungarian army. He kept up his scientific interests and his correspondence with Einstein. While recovering from diptheria, he collected his papers on the adsorption of gases by solids and submitted them as a doctoral dissertation to the University of Budapest. He later wrote an account of this period and his work, in which he explained that the war prevented him and his examiners from knowing what was going on elsewhere (*KB* p.89).

The Austro-Hungarian Empire was defeated and broken up in 1918. Hungary became a separate state but lost a lot of territory to its neighbours. In 1919 it suffered a brief Communist régime under Béla Kun, which was replaced by the authoritarian one of Admiral Horthy.

Polanyi therefore returned to Karlsruhe in 1919, and in 1920 moved to the Kaiser Wilhelm Institute for Fibre Chemistry in Berlin, where, in 1921, he married Magda Kemeny, another chemist from Hungary. Here also he expounded his potential theory of adsorption but it was rejected by the leading scientists of the time. 'Professionally, I survived the occasion only by the skin of my teeth' (*KB* p.89). From 1930 onwards Polanyi's theory began to be vindicated and adopted, although he still could not teach it as a Professor at Manchester. This episode was important in revealing to him that science, as a continuing and communal enterprise is, and has to be, governed by authority, which, of course, can make mistakes.

At the Institute he worked on the X-ray diffraction of crystals and saved his reputation and career as a scientist (*KB* Chap. 7). In 1923 he moved to the Institute for Physical Chemistry, where he became a Professor in 1926.

In 1932 Polanyi tried to involve ten other leading scientists in a protest against the dismissal of several Jewish scientists, and then resigned his positions and left Germany to take up, in 1933, the offer of the Chair in Physical Chemistry at Manchester. There he built up a noted research school, and continued to publish many scientific papers, the last (No. 218) in 1949. He was also invited to join the project to develop an atomic bomb, but was sceptical about its feasibility and refused.

Yet the Marxist belief, as expressed in Britain by J.D. Bernal and Lancelot Hogben, that science is determined by economic factors and should be planned by the State to serve technology and thence material welfare, led him to think and write (and to produce a diagrammatic film) on politics and economics, defending the freedom of science and the political and economic liberties upon which its freedom depends. In 1935 he visited Bukharin in Moscow. Bukharin, still the leading theoretician of the Communist party, told Polanyi that there is no real distinction between pure and applied science, and that in the USSR scientists would freely be led into lines of research benefitting the current Five Year Plan (*SFS* p.8). At the time Polanyi was amused by these dialectics, but his amusement ceased when Lysenko began to persecute Russian biologists for not accepting his Marxist biology.

In his *USSR Economics* of 1935 Polanyi pointed out that only production and not the whole Soviet economy was centrally planned. The Soviet economy thus recognised the need for personal judgment and mutual adjustment, and had abandoned as a failure the ideal of scientific precision. These were to become central themes of his political, economic and philosophical writings. In 1937 Polanyi went to an international scientific conference in Paris, where he observed, in the absence of scientists from Japan and the

USSR and in the attitudes of those from Germany and Italy, the growing totalitarian domination of science. In 1939 J.R. Baker published his 'A counter-blast to Bernalism', and Polanyi, who had written a criticism of Soviet science, published in 1940 as *The Contempt of Freedom*, then joined him in founding the Society for the Freedom of Science. He had already been invited to join 'The Moot' — an informal group convened by J. Oldham, and including Karl Mannheim, T.S. Eliot and several theologians — wherein he was able to formulate his philosophical ideas.

Polanyi found that the usual defences of scientific freedom were inadequate. It was necessary to attack collectivism itself, the claim of the State to control everything. In a letter of 1943 (to J.R. Baker) he argued that science can exist only in a limited State pledged to 'the guardianship of law, custom, and of our social heritage in general, to the further advancement of which — on the lines of the universal ideas underlying it — the community is dedicated' (quoted *WH*, p.427). Scepticism and Utilitarianism formed the premisses of the opponents of freedom for science as well as those of its defenders. It was necessary to go beyond such premisses to the establishment of those intangible ideals — of truth and justice — upon which depends freedom generally, and with it the freedom of science. It was therefore necessary to distinguish pure science, serving truth, from technology, serving welfare, and thence to reaffirm the right and the duty to believe in truth and our ability to attain it, as against the Sceptical denial of its reality and the Utilitarian denial of its intrinsic value. Thus Polanyi published several papers on science and freedom, free-market economics, and the law of patents. He was elected a Fellow of the Royal Society in 1944.

In 1945 he gave the Riddell Memorial Lectures at Durham, published in 1946 as *Science, Faith and Society*, a year in which, he said, he found his true vocation as a philosopher (*WH* p.426). The Vice-Chancellor of Manchester University, on his own initiative, transferred Polanyi to a new chair in 'social studies' in 1948, so that he could continue his philosophical interests without teaching duties. Polanyi had already been invited to give the Gifford Lectures at Aberdeen in 1951-2. In 1951 he published earlier essays and new material in *The Logic of Liberty*.

Through the invitation of his old friend, Arthur Koestler, Polanyi became involved in the holding of the Conference on Science and Freedom at Hamburg in 1953, and then joined the Executive Committee of the Congress of Cultural Freedom.

In 1958 the revised version of his Gifford Lectures was published as his *magnum opus, Personal Knowledge*. In that book he first set forth his distinctive account of knowing as an act of tacit integration whereby we attend *from* one set of things, the subsidiary details, and *to* another, the focal object. All knowing, he argued, has this from-to structure. We know the subsidiary details only as we use them to attend to the focal object. Therefore they are known tacitly; all knowledge has this tacit, and inexplicit, basis.

Following the publication of *Personal Knowledge*, he gave the first Lindsay Memorial Lectures at Keele, published as *The Study of Man*, 1959, wherein he extended and applied to human studies, especially history, his new philosophy of tacit integration.

In 1959 he left Manchester to become Senior Research Fellow at Merton College, Oxford. But there was much more interest in his work in the U.S.A., where he held several visiting appointments in the following fifteen years. The Terry Lectures at Yale, 1962, restating and elaborating the theory of tacit integration, were revised and published in 1966 as *The Tacit Dimension.*. Other essays of this period were collected and edited by his friend and collaborator, Dr Marjorie Grene, as *Knowing and Being*, 1969. In that year he gave two series of lectures on 'Meaning' at the Universities of Texas and Chicago. Therein he extended his account of tacit integration to the general theme of meaning, and in particular to symbols, metaphors, works of art and myths. Because of Polanyi's fading memory, Professor Harry Prosch used those lectures, with other material, for *Meaning*, 1975.

Polanyi died on February 22nd 1976. The Polanyis had two sons, George (1922-75) who followed his father as a free-market economist, and John (b.1929) who has followed him as a physical chemist and as a Fellow of the Royal Society, who now holds a chair at Toronto, and who won a joint Nobel Prize in 1986.

Polanyi came to philosophy late in life and through the pressure of political events. Thus his philosophy is unlike most contemporary philosophy in several respects:

1. It is not 'academic philosophy' in the sense of being confined to the merely technical problems of an individual philosopher or specific tradition of philosophy. Rather it is motivated by a concern for wide-spread and deep-rooted movements of thought, social life and politics.

2. Hence Polanyi gives little detailed attention to other philosophers' writings. His targets are widely held ideas and assumptions which he believes to be both wrong and dangerous. He engaged with Marxism as a political and cultural force, rather than with the particular texts of Karl Marx.

3. Scandalously, as an amateur in philosophy, he goes primarily to his own experience as a scientist, to the actual practice of scientists, to examples from the history of science, and to empirical investigations of perception, language, learning, and the like, which most British philosophers have ignored.

4. Because he is concerned to refute certain assumptions and to vindicate his own and opposing vision, he does not offer complete and separate treatises on perception, science, knowledge, politics, art, religion or any other theme of philosophy. Any and all of these topics may be incorporated in one of his books. But his work has a deep unity, so that his treatment of any one of these themes reflects his underlying concern and is not isolated from his treatments of others. As we shall see, he was much occupied with the demand for self-consistency.

Polanyi's theory of tacit integration is his distinctive contribution to philosophy, and, from *Personal Knowledge* onwards, the core of his work. Yet in a way it was a mere by-product. He did not sit down to work out a theory of knowledge; rather he found himself driven to do so as a reaction against what he felt to be wrong — dangerously wrong — in prevailing ideas and assumptions. Consequently, most of hiş works follow a similar curve: from the cultural crisis of our times (especially as it shows itself in interpretations of natural science) through an uncovering of the erroneous assumptions that are its cause, to a statement and defence of an alternative vision and thence to the possibilities for freedom, order and meaning in life and society. Tacit integration, hinted at in *The Logic of Liberty* and *Science, Faith and Society,* is first properly stated in Chapter 4 of *Personal Knowledge*, and then becomes the focal theme of later works. In some of the essays in the later parts of *Knowing and Being* it is expounded and developed more for its own sake. Yet the wider concerns remain, in introductions and epilogues or as the subjects of particular essays. Professor Prosch has presented the new material in *Meaning* in a similar context.

Perhaps the best ways into Polanyi are *The Study of Man* and the essays, 'Knowing and Being' and 'The Logic of Tacit Inference' in *Knowing and Being. Personal Knowledge,* because of its scope and Polanyi's endeavour to establish a new paradigm or vision, presents particular difficulties. But it incorporates much of the contents of *The Logic of Liberty* and *Science, Faith and Society*, and has important material which is not reproduced in later works. Consequently I propose generally to follow the argument of *Personal Knowledge* and to incorporate other items within that approach. Therefore we shall begin with the first part of the case which he deploys against 'Objectivism': that what it upholds as the model for all knowledge and as embodying its ideal — physics and chemistry — goes far beyond the limits which it sets for itself. The case is deployed specifically, but not exclusively, in the first three chapters of *Personal Knowledge*, after which Polanyi also develops his positive alternative as well as his other arguments against Objectivism.

I shall have to omit Polanyi's appeal to and citation of a mass of actual examples and empirical studies. I shall try, however, by more frequent quotation than is perhaps usual, to give the reader a taste of another distinctive feature of Polanyi's work, again especially *Personal Knowledge:* the many epigrams and aphorisms, some of them humorous, which sum up or point the argument.

2. AGAINST OBJECTIVISM

Polanyi's target in *Personal Knowledge* is Objectivism. But he is not concerned with it simply as a set of ideas and as a source of intellectual error. Rather, as becomes clear later on, especially in Chapter 7, he regards Objectivism as the source of our specifically modern ills and as that which has derailed humanitarian ideals and attempts at their realisation. The new science of the seventeenth century, which led to the rejection of many existing beliefs and of the authorities which upheld them, resulted also in a rejection of the power of belief and of authority as such, in favour of a spirit of critical independence. Knowledge and social reform were to be based upon observation and critical reason alone. But this was eventually shown to undermine science, and also all belief in truth. In the ensuing intellectual vacuum, there emerged ideologies of violence and collectivism, which reject all moral scruples and limitations upon power, for the sake of individual or national self-assertion, or to achieve some Utopia. The overthrow of Objectivism therefore becomes a moral imperative, so that we may again confidently believe in truth, freedom, justice, charity, and so forth, and be able again to act upon the courage of our convictions.

In *Science, Faith and Society*, Polanyi had shown how science itself is necessarily based upon faith, and involves a subtle and delicate interplay of individual conscience and the General Authority of the ruling scientific consensus, both dedicated to the discovery of truth. Thus he had to meet the challenge, echoed by many to this day who are fixed in Objectivist assumptions and who fail to grasp his argument, that he was thereby licensing everyone to believe anything. He denied that truth could be demonstrated: can therefore the individual call true whatever he likes, or can the State replace his personal judgment by its own?

In fact, Polanyi, in denying that truth is demonstrable, had not denied that it could be known; on the contrary he had shown how, through the exercise of conscience and in a tradition of dedication to its pursuit, truth could be known. In 1945 that was as far as he could go 'in answering the question on what grounds my convictions of the reality of truth, and of our obligations to serve the truth, are held' (*SFS* p.82).

In *Personal Knowledge* he faced the assumptions of Objectivism head on and sought to show that 'in every act of knowing there enters a passionate contribution of the person knowing what is being known' and that 'this co-efficient is no mere imperfection but a vital component of his knowledge' (*PK* p.viii). Objectivism is the belief that this personal coefficient is an imperfection, one to be reduced and, if possible, to be eliminated. It upholds an objectivity which would make knowledge a matter of the observed object alone. But in fact, and as Polanyi deals with it, Objectivism has four other elements which follow from this distrust of our personal participation in our knowing:

1.   A preference for precisely formulated knowledge, in which margins of indeterminacy are reduced or eliminated, and with them the need for personal judgment. Hence a preference for what can be measured (by instruments) and formulated mathematically, and a distrust of everything imprecise and vague.

2.   In turn there follows a tendency to Reductionism: (a) epistemologically, to what are taken to be the precise methods and observations of physics and chemistry, which become the models for all knowledge and enquiry; and (b) ontologically, to the level of merely physical reality, that studied by physics and chemistry. Otherwise put, this tendency is known as 'Scientism' and 'Mechanism'. Its modern origins go back to Galileo and Hobbes.

3.   A rejection of emotional and personal involvement, a preference for detachment, and thus a preference for 'value-free' studies as against those in which the investigator evaluates and judges his subject-matter. Evaluation is but the expression of 'subjective opinion' and not a recording of 'objective fact'. (Each

of these two phrases is a tautology in the Objectivist outlook.)
Consequently there is a sharp dichotomy of fact and value,
description and evaluation.

4. Therefore a desire to limit knowledge to what we can
physically observe: i.e. Positivism, of one form or another. But
because statements of laws of nature, and all scientific theories,
go beyond observed facts — in speaking about *all* events of a given
type or what *always* happens, or in mentioning purely inferred
entities such as sub-atomic particles — there is a tendency to deny
that they are *true* and express what really is the case. Instead, they
are interpreted, as by Ernst Mach in his *Die Mechanik* (1883), as
being merely convenient ways of referring to and thinking about
what has been or would be observed. And generally there is a
tendency to restrict more and more what is deemed to be true, and
to reinterpret as 'fruitful', 'simple', 'economical' or 'regulative'
or 'working hypotheses' the theories which science produces
and the procedures and assumptions upon which it is based.

That, then, is the total outlook which constitutes 'Objectivism'.
Its effects have been manifested in all branches of study and beyond
them in daily life. But, mostly, Objectivism exists as a set of
assumptions expressed in passing, in asides and in conversation,
rather than explicitly set out and expounded. Polanyi, in *Personal
Knowledge*, shows that the actual practices of physics and chemistry, which Objectivists believe to embody their ideal and to be a
model for all other forms of knowledge and enquiry, are much more
than the impersonal and detached recording and computation of
precise observational data. His case initially rests upon, and always
includes, an appeal to the actual facts of the history and current
practice of science.

His first target is the restriction of scientific theory to the
predicting of observable facts (i.e. element (4)), and the
assumption that a theory must be rejected as soon as any contrary
fact appears. Thereby reason is severed from experience and
theory is denied all power of revealing the rationality in nature.

Against this view, he treats in some detail the history of the discovery of relativity by Einstein (*PK* pp.9-15). Polanyi stresses the role played by pure speculation — Einstein's thinking about what would happen to an observer travelling at the speed of light — and the historical and logical irrelevance of the result of the Michelson-Morley experiment, which was often cited as the stimulus. That experiment did not give a result which would have conformed to relativity theory at all. Confirmations of the result of the experiment were made in America by D.C. Miller and his associates. But in 1925, when Miller presented his evidence, scientists ignored it, hoping that it would turn out to be wrong, for by then they could not think in terms other than the new rationality achieved by Einstein's picture of the universe.

At this point it is worth quoting Polanyi's conclusion in full:

> The   experience of D.C. Miller demonstrates quite   plainly the hollowness of the assertion that science is simply based on experiments which anybody can repeat at will. It shows that any critical verification of a scientific statement requires the same powers for recognising rationality in nature as does the process of scientific discovery, even though it exercises these at a lower level. When philosophers analyse the verification of scientific laws, they invariably choose as specimens such laws as are   not in doubt, and thus inevitably overlook the intervention of these powers. They are describing the practical demonstration of scientific law, and not its critical verification. As a result we are given an account of the scientific method which, having left out the process of discovery on the grounds that it follows no definite method, overlooks the process of verification as well, by referring only to examples where no real verification takes place (*PK* pp.13-4).

In a footnote he quotes Hans Reichenbach and H. Mehlberg as discounting discovery in favour of verification and proof. Sir Karl Popper (in *The Logic of Scientific Discovery* and elsewhere) has also argued that it is justification and the testing of hypotheses, and not induction and how theories are arrived at, which matter, both philosophically and scientifically. But Polanyi showed that no sharp distinction between discovery and verification can be made when deciding whether to accept or reject a new theory. For example, relativity, at the time of its acceptance, had made few predictions which could be verified, and it was accepted because of its inherent rationality, in deriving many known phenomena from a single principle. Relativity, quantum theory and modern physics, Polanyi claims, have put mathematics and thus rationality back into nature. For mathematical developments now anticipate what is to be found in the universe, instead of merely providing a means for computing its underlying mechanical motions.

But the false ideal of knowledge prevalent today cannot accept the rationality of nature, cannot admit it to be an essential part of scientific theory, and so glosses it over as the 'simplicity', 'symmetry', 'economy' and 'fertility' of theories. All those terms are what Polanyi calls 'pseudo-substitutions': *viz.* terms supposedly replacing others but in fact tacitly used in the same way. He quotes Hermann Weyl: 'the required simplicity is not necessarily the obvious one but we must let nature train us to recognise the true inner simplicity' (*PK* p.16). What that means is that 'simple' is to be understood in a special way which only scientists can understand, a way in which it is taken to mean 'rational', 'reasonable' or 'such that we ought to accept it' — the very terms it was supposed to replace.

Later on, in the course of distinguishing the intrinsic intellectual beauty of scientific theory, as a token of its contact with reality, from the merely formal elegance of a neater and simpler way of expressing it, he argues that fruitfulness is insufficient for distinguishing the former. For 'fruitful', as a term of appraisal applied to scientific theories, can be understood only as a pseudo-substitution for 'fruitful of *truth*'. Ptolemaic astronomy was fruitful in *error*; astrology in *income* for its practitioners; and Marxism in *power* for rulers of Communist states. And even when it is acknowledged that 'fruitful' is being used to mean 'fruitful of truth', and not anything else, it is still misleading. For a theory cannot be accepted now for the sake of the truths to which it has yet to lead, that is before those new truths have been discovered (*PK* pp.147-8). He similarly exposes the fraudulence of Kant's notion of 'regulative principles'. They are principles which, it is claimed, science uses, and perhaps needs to use, in order to discover certain things, but which are supposed not to be believed to be true of reality. For example, Kant claimed that biology needs to study the organs and organic processes of plants and animals *as if* they served the purposes of their organisms, and that biologists can do this without definitely asserting that they do serve such functions. The thesis that scientific theories are not truths but merely 'working hypotheses' or 'interpretative policies' is a development of Kant's regulative principles. But 'Kant does not say that we should entertain these generalisations as if they were true, even though we knew them to be false. His recommendation to entertain them *as if* they were true is thus seen to be based on the tacit assumption that they are in fact true... we would never use a hypothesis which we believe to be false, nor a policy we believe to be wrong' (*PK* p.307; *cf*. p.354). Such notions are pseudo-substitutions whereby people hide from themselves the fact that they do indeed believe such procedures to be right and such notions and theories to be true, even though their explicit theory of science denies this.

Polanyi's next target is the ideal of 'complete intellectual control over experience in terms of precise rules which can be formally set out and empirically tested', so that all truth and error can be ascribed to the theory and we can divest ourselves of all responsibility for it (*PK* p.18) (i.e. element (1)). Personal judgment, on such an assumption, would be superfluous and we would have only to follow the rules faithfully.

Against this Polanyi adduces two objections. The first concerns classical mechanics, which appears to require only observational data and their computation according to its formulae. However, argues Polanyi, the observational data, to which the rules and formulae are to be applied, are not themselves facts of experience. They are readings and measurements taken from instruments, which are subject both to random errors and also to systematic ones arising from individual variations in people's perceptions. And personal judgment is needed in deciding whether unaccountable discrepancies between predictions and observations (e.g. in the case of the motions of the planets before Neptune was discovered) are due to the action of unknown factors (e.g. an unknown planet) or are to be disregarded as anomalies.

The second objection is taken from quantum mechanics, the laws of which are framed in terms of probabilities. Even if the above problems did not arise, no statement of probability can be strictly contradicted by experience, because both the predicted event and its non-occurrence are compatible with such a statement. Polanyi humorously likens the behaviour of electrons when controlled by probability with the exact obedience of the dog to the command 'Come or not!' (*PK* p.21).

The question then arises as to which probabilities, numerically expressed, are to count as proving or disproving a given hypothesis. By analysing an example in detail, Polanyi shows that the standard procedures for determining this rest upon previous assessments of the intrinsic likelihood of the event in question. It would require a statistical probability, greater than that accepted in science, to convince many of the reality of extra-sensory perception from the fact that someone can guess cards before they are drawn from a pack. And some people, holding that extra-sensory perception is just not possible, would set aside any results as a mere coincidence. It is we who set, or take over from others, the level of probability which we take as sufficient to confirm or disprove a theory.

We see here the emergence of a third strand in Polanyi's case against Objectivism, specifically against element (3): the need for appraisals and evaluations in science. It is we who set standards for the evaluation of experimental results as significant or not, for the data themselves do not tell us this. Standards of scientific significance and accuracy have emerged in history — comparatively recent history — and are not universally followed. It is we who decide just what degrees of accuracy and precision are needed in any given context. For there is no such thing as total precision or accuracy. In science there is always a margin of indeterminacy and error, just as in engineering there is always a margin of tolerance. ('Precision engineering' claims to achieve only small tolerances and not to have eliminated them.) And we can decide what degree of accuracy is required only by our personal sense of what is fitting, or by our personal acceptance of someone else's judgment. For there can never be precise rules to tell us what degree of precision is required (*PK* pp.251-2).

As we have seen, it is we who have to decide what, generally and in each case, is to count as a significant degree of probability such that we shall accept, reject, more confidently believe or be more dubious about, a scientific hypothesis. Now attempts have been made, by Keynes and others, to provide rules for according credence to evidence. These deal with statements of the probability of hypothesis H in relation to evidence E, formulated as $P(H/E)$. But this, argues Polanyi, is only a partial formalisation of the personal act of appraising probabilities. On the one hand, such statements are impersonal, being asserted by no one, and so are incomplete and need to be endorsed by us as we use them (a general principle which we shall consider further in Chapter 4). On the other hand, we still need to pick out, purely by personal judgment, those hypotheses which are most likely to be true, for life does not permit scientists to start testing hypotheses at random. 'To select good questions for investigation is the mark of scientific talent, and any theory of inductive inference in which this talent plays no part is a *Hamlet* without the prince' (*PK* p.30).

This, we note, is just what Popper omits in dismissing as logically irrelevant the processes whereby a theory is first formulated. And it also tells against his claim that scientists try to falsify rather than prove, and therefore pick the least probable (i.e. the most risky) hypotheses. Polanyi comments (*TD* p.78) that it contradicts the whole aim of science to make *discoveries*. Popper, it seems, was still the prisoner of Objectivist assumptions in being unprepared to state outright that science aims at, can attain, and has attained what is *true*.

Similar considerations apply to verification: 'Things are not labelled ''evidence'' in nature, but are evidence only to the extent to which they are accepted as such by us as observers' (*PK* p.43). Seeing is not inevitably believing, as illustrated by the example which Polanyi gives of Challis, who did observe the undiscovered planet suggested by Leverrier and Adams, but who took no notice of his observations for he distrusted their hypothesis, the one he was seeking to verify.

The assessment of probabilities presupposes a capacity to distinguish and recognise chance and order, the theme of Chapter 3 of *Personal Knowledge*. Polanyi illustrates this by 'Welcome to Wales' set out in pebbles at a railway station. The probability of this having happened by chance is so remote that it would never be accepted. But what about the arrangement they would take if the garden had been neglected for some time? That too would be one out of a very large number of possibilities, but we would not say that that did not happen by chance. This reveals the tacit assumption made about the former: only when we recognise a distinctive pattern does the question arise as to whether it happened by chance. Generally, we can say that past events were improbable, such as the fulfilment of a horoscope, only if we recognise in them a distinct pattern, and then deny the reality of the pattern, saying that they occurred at random within many possibilities. Polanyi illustrates the interactions of randomness and order with examples from statistical thermodynamics and kinetics, and shows that our ability to distinguish the two cannot be derived from numerical probabilities, for the calculus of probabilities itself presupposes an ability to recognise randomness in nature.

The recognition of order in nature also illustrates the error of Objectivism in denying the intrinsic rationality of nature, so that scientific theory and mathematics become merely convenient means of predicting and computing observations. Polanyi gives the examples of chemical proportions, as in chemical formulae, which are expressed as ratios of integers, and of the classification of crystals according to the types of geometrical symmetry which they embody.

Polanyi, then, has presented a formidable case, based on physics and chemistry, against elements (1) and (4) of the Objectivist ideal: respectively, the demand for precisely formulated knowledge, and the limitation of knowledge to what can be confirmed and falsified by observation. But there remain the two other elements which we have distinguished. We shall leave the theme of Reductionism (element (2)), for consideration in Chapter 5, along with Polanyi's own ontology and cosmology. Let us now turn to some parts of Chapter 6 of *Personal Knowledge,* 'Intellectual Passions', to see his case, from the practice of science, against the denial of the *passionate* involvement of the knower in his knowing.

In this chapter Polanyi's aim is to show that intellectual emotions have a constitutive and guiding role in scientific discovery and other domains of enquiry and life, and are not merely by-products of the scientist's work.

As we noted earlier, Polanyi came to philosophy in order to articulate a defence of the freedom of science. That meant accrediting science with the power to attain truth about nature and a valuation of that truth. If we generally have no interest in the truth, then we shall not value science, but only technology, which aids us to achieve other things, such as comfort or world-domination. Polanyi now focuses on the inherent intellectual beauty of scientific theory as a token of its contact with reality. This aligns science with art and other cultural achievements and requires a justification of the passionate valuations on which they rest.

> Science can then no longer hope to survive on an island of positive facts, around which the rest of man's intellectual heritage sinks to the status of subjective emotionalism. It must claim that certain emotions are right; and if it can make good such a claim, it will not only save itself but sustain by its example the whole system of cultural life of which it forms part (*PK*, p.134).

A body of purely detached knowledge would be valued by no

one. This is the first of four functions performed by emotion in the practice of science: upholding the value of science itself. The other three functions are: the selection of data, problems and theories of scientific value; motivating and sustaining the endeavour to cross the logical gap between present knowledge and something yet to be discovered; and convincing others of the reality of that discovery.

We have already noted that scientists must select hypotheses which seem likely to be true, for they cannot waste time on seeking to verify them all. But, within the range of the plausible, there is a need to distinguish the more interesting from the less. For talents and resources would otherwise be dissipated in accumulating largely unconnected observations, with little bearing on anything else. Polanyi states that there are three bases of value in science: certainty or accuracy, systematic relevance or profundity, and the extra-scientific one of intrinsic interest. These three are realised somewhat unevenly in the different branches of natural science: biology, for example, is generally weaker in the first two but richer in the third. Polanyi cites examples to show that mere accuracy is insufficient, for publication, prizes or further investigation. Now no strict rules can be given for evaluating scientific value, so that it is a matter of fallible judgment — individual and collective — as to what should be accepted and studied further, and what should be ignored. Polanyi refers to the problem, presented in biology and human studies, of the clash between the intrinsic interest of life and mind and their frequent resistance to precise observation and measurement. If the latter are preferred, then all that will be produced will be irrelevant to the subject-matter and of no interest in itself — something that can be easily illustrated from books and articles on psychology, sociology and the theory of education.

The selection of a problem for investigation requires an intimation of what it is likely to lead to, and of the scientific value of the result. The selective function transforms itself into the heuristic function — the urge to discover and to discover something of interest, and the sustaining of that urge through the ups and downs of a protracted period of research. Polanyi focuses upon major innovations, such as those of Kepler and Einstein, where there is a definite logical gap to be crossed between existing conceptions and new ones needed for articulating discoveries which change a whole way of seeing things. Such discoveries, I would add, cannot be made in a detached, uninvolved and uninterested manner, whereas routine work, in any field, can be conducted in such a way. But nothing significant can be discovered by routine operations, or recognised if found by chance by one whose work and outlook is merely one of routine. Yet that is precisely what Objectivism would reduce science to — the mechanical and impersonal carrying out of a set of specific and precise operations, just like a production-line in a factory.

Having made his discovery, the scientist does not keep it to himself but seeks to communicate it to others. This is the persuasive function of emotion in science. Again, it is especially needed when the discovery is a major innovation. For the discoverer now has to convince his colleagues to see things in a new light, to cross the logical gap from what they already know to what he has discovered. In matters of routine, or not much beyond it, this presents few problems, and requires only an ordinary interest in new work. But when a whole shift in outlook is required, then the discovery cannot be demonstrated in the terms of existing theories. His colleagues have to learn a new language so that they can understand what he is talking about. But they have to learn it before they can verify for themselves that there is something real and important to be learned, and thus they have to have an initial sympathy and trust in their colleague who claims to have made a radical discovery. (The same applies to anyone learning something quite new to him, such as Polanyi's own learning to understand X-ray plates of lungs along with what his teachers meant when they talked about them — *PK* p.10.) The discoverer has to use or evoke that sympathy, or to dispel or discredit others' hostility, motivated by a fear that the new way of thinking will lead them into error. Hence arises the unedifying spectacle of scientific controversies, of which Polanyi gives several examples. But these could not arise if emotions were not there, and needed, in the first place.

This survey of the functions of emotion in science not only demonstrates the knower's necessarily passionate engagement in his knowing but also gives more examples of the need for the exercise of personal judgment, especially in the case of the third function. We see this in a significant feature of great controversies: *viz.* the temptation to discredit the claimed innovation as 'not being science'. (Philosophers more frequently make parallel remarks.) But no exact criterion of demarcation can be given for what is science and what is not. Popper has argued for falsifiability, and we can see in some cases — e.g. Marx and Marxism — the self-delusory shifts which some people practise in order not to accept that some of their claims have been refuted. Polanyi gives examples of these, within science and without, in Chapter 9, §9 and §10, of *Personal Knowledge*, and shows that the illegitimate moves are abuses of necessary ones, and that there can be no rule for sorting out the one from the other. As we have seen, some aspects of natural science are not amenable to any obvious falsification, and science has to proceed at times by ignoring contrary evidence, hoping that one day it will be shown to be irrelevant or false. Consequently, there is no easy rule whereby to demarcate science from non-science — e.g. extra-sensory perception which some refuse even to consider as a scientific possibility. (Yet a Chair in Para-normal Psychology has recently been established at Edinburgh.) We have to use our personal judgment to decide if there is anything real and worthwhile in such a domain. Another type of case, frequently mentioned here by Polanyi, is the distrust, especially in chemistry, of speculative reasoning, despite the fact that chemistry was mostly founded on the speculations of Dalton, Kekulé and van't Hoff (*PK* p.156). For it requires great delicacy to distinguish the power of the intellectual beauty of theory to reveal what nature is, from its merely formal attractiveness as a convenient way of summarising existing knowledge (*PK* p.143).

Physics and chemistry, Polanyi has shown, do not and cannot meet the Objectivist ideals of detached and precise observations and predictions of nature. If those attracted to such ways of thinking face these facts squarely, then they will give up either their Objectivist assumptions or most of the results and practice of modern science. What is likely often to happen is that they will concede something of the case while it is being presented, yet later, and especially outside science, they will continue to express and apply their Objectivist assumptions. What Polanyi had to do was to widen his argument and to show how all our knowing is, and must be, quite different from the Objectivist ideal. He begins that positive task in Chapter 4 of *Personal Knowledge*.

3. KNOWING AS A PERSONAL ACHIEVEMENT

In Chapter 4 of *Personal Knowledge* Polanyi turns to the widening of his argument and the establishment of an alternative account of knowledge as a personal achievement. We have seen him draw attention to aspects of science for which there are no rules and where we must rely on personal judgment. Polanyi now argues that all knowing has its tacit dimensions, such that no fully explicit and thus wholly critically tested body of knowledge can exist. *'We know more than we can tell'* (*TD* p.4) becomes the heart of his message. But why is this so? Why must much of what we know remain hidden to us?

The answer lies in Polanyi's discovery of two radically different forms of knowing and of the relationship between them. Awareness has not just a dyadic relation between the knower and the object known, but a triadic one, in which the knower attends *from* one set of things to another. Polanyi's first example is the use of a hammer to drive in a nail (*PK* p.55). In doing this we are aware of both the hammer and the nail but in very different ways. We watch the nail: we focus our attention upon it. But we feel the handle of the hammer in our hands while using it. And when we hit the nail, we feel the impact of the head of the hammer on the nail rather than of the handle of the hammer upon our hands. We do not *watch* the hammer, yet we are aware of it in hitting the nail. What we feel guides us in the use of the hammer, yet we do not focus upon those feelings. Rather, we attend *from* them and to the nail. We have a *focal awareness* of the nail, and of what is happening to it, and a *subsidiary awareness* of the hammer and its impact upon our hands. But, and this is very important, these two forms of awareness do not occur merely side by side as do marginal and focal awareness in one's field of vision. For they are *functionally* related. The subsidiary awareness of the hammer in the hand is merged into our focal awareness of the nail as we use the former in attending to and driving in the latter.

Polanyi's second example is the use of a probe to explore a cavity. We find out the size and shape of the cavity, not by focusing upon the impact of the probe upon our fingers, but upon the point of the probe, and thence in turn upon the walls of the cavity. We attend *from*, and *with*, our fingers and the probe to the cavity. In learning to use a probe, we learn to shift our focal attention from the probe itself to what we explore with it. We do not then cease to be aware of the probe, but are aware of it subsidiarily. We project ourselves into the hammer or the tip of the probe. It then becomes the *distal* term of the tacit relation, our hands or fingers being the *proximal* term.

The radical difference between these two forms of attention, and their integration, can be seen in what happens when we shift our attention back from the formerly focal object to what we were attending from. If he starts to watch his hands, the pianist gets confused and may have to stop. Likewise the actor afflicted by stage-fright focuses his attention upon the next word rather than the whole sentence, speech and scene. The stutterer's difficulties multiply as his affliction focuses his attention on the sound to be produced, and how he is to produce it, rather than upon the meaning he intends to express. Making the subsidiarily known details into objects of focal attention sooner or later destroys their integration into the task to be performed or in the object to be known.

In his several expositions of tacit integration Polanyi gave many instances of people's ability to do and to recognise something while being unable to say how they do or recognise it. For instance, the example of a psychiatrist who could distinguish genuine from hysterical epileptic fits but could not tell his students how to do this (*KB* p.123). One of my aunts used to sex day-old chicks. It mattered greatly to the farmer that she could do this accurately, for he sold them as correctly sorted hens or cocks. Yet there are no visible signs at hatching to distinguish them. She could sort them, and be proved right afterwards, but could not say how she knew which was which. Nor could Polanyi say how he recognised his macintosh from several others just like it (presumably in the days when they were all Burberrys). Again, when he began these investigations, no one could tell him how cyclists maintain their balance. And, of course, if one does know the rule explicitly, as Polanyi formulated it, one cannot, when riding, explicitly bring it to mind and make the required measurements and calculations (*PK* pp.49-50). Likewise we know the rules of our mother-tongue only in using them to speak correctly. If we have learned another language by formal methods, we cease to recall the rules as formulated when we begin to speak fluently, and then may forget them as formulae. All explicit rules and maxims lapse into unconsciousness as we become adept at the relevant task.

Perception is likewise a tacit integration of subsidiarily known details into focal awareness of the object perceived, and therefore a skilful performance. These details are parts or aspects of the object perceived, aspects of the context in which it and the perceiver are placed, and events within the perceiver himself, such as the slight differences between the two retinal images which give us stereoscopic vision. Psychological investigation reveals the rules and clues which we use and the many adjustments which we make, in order to perceive a world of solid, persisting and relatively constant objects. In trick situations we continue to use the clues in the usual way, and thus misperceive an inflating balloon, against a featureless background, as a ball approaching us, or, in a room with false perspective, see a boy becoming taller than a man. In perception we are never explicitly aware of many of the clues and procedures which we use, but know them only as we use them in trying to perceive the world, and certainly are not explicitly aware of our use of them. Subjects wearing left-right or up-down inverting spectacles learn to cease to attend to their visual images and to attend *from* them, re-integrating their vision with their bodily movement, and thus coping with the world. They accomplish this feat, not by explicit reasoning about taking left for right or down for up, but by the effort to cope with what they touch and bump into. If asked about it, they report that they still see inverted images but are no longer aware of this until asked and having to think about it (*KB* pp.198-9).

While he takes over the facts revealed by Gestalt psychology, Polanyi rejects its explanation of them in terms of processes of automatic equilibration in the nervous system. For that explanation glosses over the difference between veridical and illusory perception and does not account for the personal effort made by the perceiver (*PK* pp.98, 340-1). While much of perception occurs automatically, it is still a power that we have achieved in infancy, and which at moments we have to deploy more deliberately, with some degree of self-awareness and with effort. It is something we *do*, and therefore do well or ill, easily or with effort, responsibly or irresponsibly. Likewise with all our intellectual activities.

In *The Tacit Dimension*, Chapter 1, Polanyi set out three consequent structures of tacit integration:

1.   The *phenomenal* structure whereby the details take on a new appearance as we perceive them as parts of a whole. Camouflage works by breaking up the characteristic outline of something into mere patches of colour — what Empiricist philosophers assume to be still our primary objects of attention. But as we attend from these patches to the thing itself, so, if we succeed, the outline of the thing emerges. Likewise from photographs of pieces of a face, which as separate pictures mean nothing more to us, a familiar face emerges as, physically or imaginatively, we put them together.

2.   The *semantic* function. The familiar face is then the meaning of the individual photographs. Likewise the shape of the cavity is the meaning of the impact of the probe on our fingers. By tacit integration of the details we interpret their joint significance. This is the *semantic* aspect of tacit integration. It, too, is destroyed by a shift of focus to the details themselves. For example, if we attend to a word in and by itself, as in repeating it several times, it loses its

meaning. We can regain that meaning only by ceasing to attend to the word and by starting to attend from it and to its meaning, as by using it in a sentence.

3.   The *ontological* structure. The object itself, structured by its subsidiary details, is also an integration of them into the comprehensive whole, or complex performance, which it itself is. We shall follow this up in Chapter 5.

By attending from its details, along with others, to the object itself we re-create its own organisation. Thereby we *interiorise* and *indwell* its details. Polanyi aligns this indwelling of focal objects to the indwelling of tools, such as hammers and probes. As we use, attend from and project ourselves into these tools, we incorporate them in our bodies and for the moment they become parts of us. Likewise we indwell our intellectual frameworks — the organisations of our perceptual fields, symbolic systems, conceptions, schemata, classifications, principles of reasoning — by means of which we understand the world. I would term 'primary indwelling' this use of our bodies, perceptual organs and intellectual frameworks, in contrast to the 're-constituting' or 're-performing' indwelling whereby we comprehend objects and events outside ourselves. As we shall see, indwelling has many degrees of depth. But we can see immediately that knowing as a (re-constituting) indwelling of the object known overcomes the sharp dichotomy of subject and object, knower and the known, which has dominated philosophy since Descartes.

Let us now summarise the relations between the subsidiary and focal elements in our knowing. The following summary will also answer the objection that it is self-contradictory to speak about (i.e. to claim to know) what we do not know that we know.

1.   The focal elements can be made explicit, articulated and stated, if we have or invent the required vocabulary or other symbolic systems (maps, diagrams, charts). Infants and animals cannot make any of their focal knowledge explicit, since they lack language.

2.   The subsidiary elements are only implicitly known when we

actually use them. At another time, by analysis of what we do and focusing upon the details, we may come to know them explicitly. This is what driving instructors, grammarians and sports coaches have to do. Again, one person can analyse another's tacit integrations and make explicit what the latter knows only tacitly: e.g. those syllables, in a string of nonsense, which subjects learn to recognise as preceding an electric shock, but which they cannot identify in themselves (*TD* pp.7-8).

3. But at the same time, in some cases, we may have a latent knowledge, an awareness 'at the back of our minds', that we are employing some items of knowledge or skills, of a general sort, while not, there and then, being able to specify them in detail. For example, the pianist is clearly aware that he is using his fingers. But he is not explicitly aware which finger is now pressing which key — only the beginner has that awareness. Polanyi could read his letters in the morning, without noticing what language they were written in (*PK* p.57). Formal education provides us with an extensive vocabulary and body of knowledge. We know that we know many words, but never just how many and which ones, and likewise we know the sorts of thing that we know, but cannot specify every item (*PK* p.103).

4. There is a core of knowledge which never can be specified and made explicit: *viz.* how we integrate a set of subsidiarily known details or rules (which may be specifiable at another time or by another person) into what we focally know or perform. As Kant and Ryle knew, no explicit rule can tell you how and when to apply it; no scheme or conception can tell you how to resolve borderline cases in deciding what is and is not an instance of it. We can know all the particulars in a three-dimensional aggregate — e.g. the parts of the human body or of a complex machine, or the geological strata of a region — but cannot specify and know explicity just how each is related spatially to the rest. No verbal or diagrammatic representation can be adequate, and the more complex and detailed a three-dimensional model becomes, the more it reproduces the very problem to be solved (*PK* pp.89-90).

These last are examples of the necessarily tacit dimensions of all articulate thought — of all the knowledge that we can put into language or other symbolic systems, and so hold up explicitly before our minds. Polanyi treats them at length in Chapter 5 of *Personal Knowledge*. Here I shall consider only a few instances.

1.   Contrary to what Wittgenstein said in the *Tractatus*, nothing that can be said can be said clearly. All language and symbolic representation have a margin of interdeterminacy. All thought involves classification and thus the resolution of boderline cases, no matter how strict are the explicit rules laid down. And we can never anticipate them all in advance (*PK* pp.89-90). For words and other symbols have to be general terms, and not the proper names of evanescent sense-data (such as patches of colour) which Russell once thought they should be, and thus we have to decide, without further rules, when and whether they apply or not. They are all 'open-textured' to some extent, and it is the user who has to impose limits upon their use according to his sense of their fitness for the reality which is to be expressed by means of them (*PK* p.113). A word that is totally open and so can be used to refer to anything, means nothing: a word that refers just to this sense-datum here and now, is useless.

2.   Thus it is also an act of personal judgment, for which there can be no specifiable rules, to decide when to extend the use of a term or not. For example, birds that have a distinctive feature previously unrecorded, may be just a sport, a new sub-species or a new species, and so we must decide whether they are to be called by the old name, the old name with a new adjective, or an entirely new name. We have to decide if and how the idea, and thence the law, of copyright can apply to evanescent products such as radio programmes; whether heavy hydrogen is or is not a new isotope; whether science and theology, and not just 'Lexicon' and crosswords, are to be regarded as language-games.

3.   It also requires personal judgment to decide if a new locution is or is not meaningful. To the ordinary mind 'the square root of -1' is nonsense, but mathematicians found it had a meaning after all.

4.   And mathematics, the most formalized and articulate body of knowledge, has to be learned, as we all knew at school and later, by practice in applying the explicit rules in solving particular problems. It is not enough merely to restate the rules and formulae. Hence mastery of mathematics is the acquiring of an art which cannot itself be reduced to specified and explicit rules and formulae (*PK* p.125).

Articulate and therefore explicit knowledge is controlled and employed by tacit and personal judgments and decisions. All knowing is therefore sustained by an art, a skilful practice. Knowing that something is the case involves knowing how to perceive, think, recognise, classify, re-classify, interpret, reinterpret, apply a scheme (Piaget's 'assimilation'), alter the scheme to suit the object (Piaget's 'adaptation'), and correctly to apply or reinterpret a vocabulary. Any statement of what we know has to be guided by these skills. In specifying and stating these skills here and now, I am using them without attending to each as I use it — e.g. in the very moment that I choose and then reject a given word, I attend to that word and not to my sense of its suitability, which I am using in choosing and rejecting it. Therefore, because it always involves skilful performances, knowledge can never be rendered wholly explicit and removed entirely from its tacit roots. Immediately we make something explicit there forms around it a new shell of tacit elements which sustain it. Words, charts and maps mean nothing in themselves: they mean something only to and for minds which can interpret them.

This is the error in Popper's account of 'World 3', the 'objective knowledge', in the book of that title, which is not known by anyone but is in books, notes, maps and so on. On the contrary, none of it is knowledge, as may be seen by the thought-experiment of imagining the vanishing of all intelligence from the universe while the physical texts remain. Three personal acts are required to actualise the potential knowledge recorded in books: (a) reading; (b) understanding what is read; and (c) believing what is understood. No book conveys anything to the illiterate, nor to those who cannot read the language in which it is written. Nor is reading sufficient, as may be seen by reading a work on something about which one knows nothing — 'It's all Greek to me'. No book can tell you how to understand it, and understanding requires the possession and deployment of an intellectual framework — schemata and conceptions — to which we assimilate what we read, and, perhaps, which we may have to adapt to some part of what we read. And even when understood, the contents of a text may be dismissed as erroneous and not accepted as knowledge, as Popper would dismiss the contents of books of astrology. Books are therefore only records of knowledge and do not contain actual knowledge. Hence 'objective knowledge' is lost, even though the physical texts remain, if the traditions are lost which keep alive the essentially tacit knowledge of literacy and understanding. For no book can teach you to read, and mere literacy is not enough for understanding. Thus Greek texts continued to exist in Latin Europe in the Dark Ages, but only few understood the language and still fewer, if any, much of the subject-matter. The knowledge recorded in them had to be slowly and painfully regained. Borges has a story of an Arab scholar in Andalucia who is commenting on Aristotle's *Poetics*, and who reproduces the division of poetry into epic and drama. It is clear that he knows nothing of acting and plays. He then hears a story from a traveller about something which the reader understands as being a description of actors and acting. But it means nothing to the scholar who returns to the *Poetics* unenlightened. So much for 'objective knowledge'!

Now the three personal acts of reading (or deciphering), understanding and believing are essentially tacit ones. No book can teach the illiterate to read (nor can you learn your mother-tongue from formulated rules). As Plato pointed out, no book can answer a question which you put to it, and oral teaching and practical coaching are required for transmitting literacy and other skills. (I once sat for an hour stuck on page one of the Ladybird book on knitting, complete with illustration, before I dragged up a dim memory from boyhood and made sense of the instructions about casting on.) Moreover, as we noted above with reference to mathematics, such coaching is needed for all forms of articulate knowledge as well. Schools and universities cannot simply issue reading-lists and direct students to their libraries. Hence Polanyi draws attention to the importance of tradition for sustaining science and other articulate bodies of knowledge.

Tacit knowledge cannot be explicitly taught. It can be passed on only by being manifested in practice and through the relationship of accredited master and attentive apprentice:

> By watching the master and emulating his efforts in the presence of his example, the apprentice unconsciously picks up the rules of the art, including those which are not explicitly known to the master himself. These hidden rules can be assimilated only by a person who surrenders himself to that extent uncritically to the imitation of another (*PK* p.53).

Hence the need for a living tradition to pass on tacit knowledge across the generations. When such a tradition is broken, it is a very difficult task to reconstruct and rediscover what has been lost. Similarly, the history of science is one of fits and starts by relatively isolated individuals until, in the sixteenth and seventeenth centuries, a continuous and therefore accumulative tradition was established. And 'while *the articulate contents of science* are successfully taught all over the world in hundreds of new universities, *the unspecifiable art of scientific research* has not yet penetrated to many of these' (*PK* p.53). As one can see in many parts of Africa, where machines are run until they break down without thought for regular maintenance, it is not enough just to ship machines abroad if there is no tradition of technology. And the same applies to all human activities. Africa is also littered with abandoned constitutions.

Finally, for now, the comment that this has all been said before — by the later Wittgenstein, Oakeshott or Ryle, with his distinction between 'knowing that' and 'knowing how'. The answer is, 'Yes and No'. On the one hand, many philosophers (and thousands of ordinary people) have become aware of knowing things which they cannot state. On the other hand, there are two significant differences: (a) few have paid continued attention to this fact, and still less have argued from it, while some have shied away from it; and (b) none has articulated the distinction of the two forms of knowing and their relation to each other. Polanyi himself pointed out that Kant, 'so powerfully bent on strictly determining the rules of pure reason', had to admit that personal judgment, and not yet further rules, must apply rules, and likewise must apply the schema of a class to instances which are thereby identified as members of it, and that this ability is inscrutable (*KB* pp.105-6). But, almost alone, Polanyi focuses upon such facts and argues at length for them — indeed, founds his philosophy upon the tacit dimensions of our knowing. I say 'almost alone' for Merleau-Ponty's *The Phenomenology of Perception* is, in part, a sustained argument against the thesis that knowing is knowing that we know. And positively he shows that we use our bodies, sense organs, perceptions and motor habits, which we take for granted and of which we are not normally explicitly aware, while we focus upon the world. Referring to pathological cases, he shows us the disintegration which results from the reversal of our normal direction of attention. On virtually every theme he and Polanyi coincide, yet, as Polanyi himself noted in several places, Merleau-Ponty never quite formulated the distinction between attending from and attending to, and the integration of these two modes of attention in all our knowing and action.

4. THE FIDUCIARY PROGRAMME

Tacit knowledge is also and necessarily *personal* knowledge, knowledge achieved and sustained by a person. As we have seen in relation to Popper's 'World 3', there can be no impersonal knowledge which is not the knowledge possessed by someone. Nor can there be any knowledge which is not the achievement of someone, something which he has shaped and assimilated. And there is no knowledge which is not *believed* by someone. Mere rote learning and repetition result in knowing with little understanding and often with little belief in what is stated. That is what Objectivism would reduce knowledge to — the churning out of mere sounds and marks. Indeed, Behaviourism, one of the most important products of Objectivism today, does reduce knowledge to merely verbal repetition.

But to speak of belief is to raise again fears of 'subjectivism'. In the modern age 'mere belief' has been opposed to 'knowledge'. Knowledge is commonly asserted to be 'justified true belief', that is belief, which is both true and supported by evidence. And the task of philosophy has been to justify, as far as it can, our ordinary or scientific beliefs. But, as we have seen, our knowledge, being more than we can tell, rests upon foundations which we can never examine and so can never 'justify'.

Polanyi therefore has the task of removing this critical suspicion of belief. This is what he calls his 'fiduciary programme', which involves also a very different conception of the task of philosophy. We shall now trace his argument against the Objectivist erosion of our power to believe, which is the special theme of Part 3 (Chapters 8 to 10) of *Personal Knowledge,* 'The Justification of Personal Knowledge'. Later on (*TD* p.x) Polanyi said that his elaboration of the structure of tacit knowing reduced his reliance upon the necesity of commitment as argued in *Personal Knowledge*. But I think that nothing which he wrote afterwards in any way reduced the validity and importance of his earlier argument.

In Chapter 2 we saw how Polanyi exposed the evasions of the pseudo-substitutions for truth such as 'simplicity' and 'regulative principles'. Now in the from-to structure of tacit knowing, we use and hence rely upon the subsidiary details. We commit ourselves to them as we commit ourselves to a bridge when crossing a river. Likewise we are committed, whether we realise it or not, to the general reliability of our perceptual organs, sensory-motor system, intellectual frameworks, native language, and acquired skills and information, all of which we use in knowing and doing other things. And, as we have also seen, knowledge is not knowledge if not believed.

In Chapter 8 Polanyi brings out the tacit and personal affirmations necessary in our use of language. For explicit knowledge, recorded in writing, maps, charts and the like, appears to be simply there and so impersonal. But it is one thing to utter a statement and another to believe it. A parrot which utters, 'Snow is white', is not expressing a truth but merely uttering certain sounds. Now normally we say simply 'Snow is white', and we are taken to be stating a truth which we believe, unless there are indications to the contrary, such as acting in a play or setting out another's argument which we have not yet endorsed. Our personal subscription to what we say is normally tacit and taken for granted. And, Polanyi argues, this must be the case. Thus '"Snow is white" is true' is not itself a factual statement of the same order as 'Snow is white'. It is a reassertion of 'Snow is white' wherein the utterer explicitly endorses that proposition. It is an act which he performs and not a fact which he observes. Thus there cannot arise the infinite regress, continuing with '"'Snow is white' is true" is true', which would follow were the utterance of '"Snow is white" is true' a statement of fact like 'Snow is white'. It is like a signature on a cheque rather than like a statement. And it must be personal, just as there cannot be impersonal signatures and impersonal cheques.

Similarly in all use of language we tacitly put our endorsement into what we say, unless we explicitly cancel it, as by using 'alleged', 'so-called' or quotation marks. The former is the confident use of language and the latter the sceptical or oblique use. But, while we can question any term by itself, we can never question all. 'The "cat" sat on the mat' does say something significant, but 'The "cat" allegedly sat on the so-called mat' means nothing.

Again, in using calculators, inference machines, computers, measuring instruments, and marking schemes, we tacitly rely on them. In themselves they say and do nothing of significance. In quoting what comes out of a computer, we tacitly trust (a) the accuracy and truth of what was put into it ('junk in, junk out'), and (b) the validity of the operations performed upon it in accordance with the program. It is we who give a meaning to, and who endorse the truth and validity of what is then meant, to the marks that it churns out. Likewise we trust the axioms used in a mathematical calculation, or the rules used in an inference.

Now none of this can be explicitly stated without involving an infinite regress, as Lewis Carroll showed concerning the attempt to make a rule of inference into an explicit premise of an inference wherein it is used ('What the Tortoise said to Achilles' *Mind*, 1895). Our endorsement and confident use of language, principles of reasoning, computers and all other tools and machines, is a tacit act and necessarily so.

This means that the Objectivist ideal of a fully tested and critically established body of knowledge is a delusion. On the one hand, there are many subsidiary clues which we only tacitly know in attending *from* them. On the other, we can never focus upon, make explicit and critically examine the items of knowledge, principles, instruments and so forth that we use in testing. If you doubt the accuracy of a watch or ruler, you test it against another *which you thereby do not doubt but confidently rely upon.* You implicitly rely upon the second and therefore a-critically trust it. Note, not 'uncritically' — for that implies that it could be critically used. But what is used is trusted and is, not there and then, an object of examination. Now we can use something in order to test it, as the mechanic does with the brakes of a car. But in using them like this, he puts a provisional trust in them, which he endorses or withholds afterwards. Likewise, we can use a principle in order to refute it by means of a *reductio ad absurdum*. We act as if we believed it to be true or valid. But in doing this we confidently and a-critically use other principles, such as that of an argument to absurdity, where there is no 'as if' about them.

Here, then, is the core of Polanyi's 'post-critical' philosophy — the restoration of our power to believe which has been eroded by Objectivism and the Scepticism in which its impossible ideal results. Polanyi reinstates the Augustinian principle of *nisi credideritis, non intelligitis*: 'Unless you believe, you will not understand' (*PK* p.266). Belief is prior to demonstration and criticism. If nothing is to be trusted without examination, then there can be no examinations and nothing can be examined. If nothing is to be believed without evidence, then nothing can be believed and there can be no evidence. For by calling something 'evidence' we thereby endorse it, and ultimately we tacitly and a-critically endorse it, as both itself true and supporting what it is cited as evidence for.

> This then is our liberation from Objectivism: to realise that we can voice our ultimate convictions only from within our convictions — from within the whole system of acceptances that are logically prior to the holding of any particular piece of knowledge. If an ultimate logical level is to be attained and made explicit, this must be a declaration of my personal beliefs. I believe that the function of philosophic reflection consists in bringing to light, and affirming as my own, the beliefs implied in such of my thoughts and practices as I believe to be valid; that I must aim at discovering what I truly believe in and at formulating the convictions which I find myself holding; that I must conquer my self-doubt, so as to retain a firm hold on this programme of self-identification (*PK* p.267).

Polanyi thereby rejects the whole critical programme of modern philosophy from Descartes onwards — the futile endeavour to 'found' and 'justify' at least some part of what we ordinarily claim to know. That endeavour, as the course of modern philosophy soon proved, resulted in the progressive diminution of knowledge, and must logically end in total scepticism and aphasia. For:

> Innocently, we had trusted that we could be relieved of all personal responsibility for our beliefs by objective criteria of validity — and our critical powers have shattered this hope.... The alternative to this, which I am seeking to establish here, is to restore to us once more the power for the deliberate holding of unproven beliefs' (*PK* p.268).

Consequently he takes for his next target the Cartesian programme of systematic doubt.

That programme, we may note, cannot be carried out, and it results in philosophy being conducted in bad faith. For Descartes, while attempting to test everything by the method of doubt, stated that he would not give up his ordinary beliefs in the meantime and before he had established them beyond doubt, and Hume locked away the destructive conclusions of his philosophy and went to forget them by playing backgammon. The philosophy of doubt is one that cannot be lived. Polanyi quotes passages from J.S. Mill and Betrand Russell on claims not to believe what can be doubted and against dogmatism. But, he comments, authors such as this merely cover up by that sort of declaration their own adherence to beliefs which, on their own principles, are unfounded or dogmatic (*PK* pp.270-1). For doubting one explicit proposition implies rejecting it in favour of others. This is obvious with regard to contradiction: 'I believe *p*' (e.g. that all men are mortal) is contradicted by 'I believe not-p' (that all men are not mortal). Here belief and disbelief are logically equivalent. As for agnostic doubt, it is either temporary ('I believe *p* is not proven'), which leaves open the possibility of proof in the future, or permanent ('I believe *p* cannot be proven'). In both cases there is an implicit belief in what constitutes proof and how it can and cannot be attained. Polanyi then proceeds to give examples, from science and other activities, of reasonable and unreasonable agnosticism and scepticism. These, and examples of discovery by believing even more firmly in what is already accepted (e.g. Columbus and the sphericity of the world and thus the possibility of circumnavigation), show that neither belief nor doubt can be universally effective in leading to discoveries.

Objectivism, tolerating no overt declarations of belief, forces people today back into the frame of mind of primitive peoples, whereby they can reject what to us are obvious refutations of some of their basic assumptions, such as the efficacy of spells and oracles. They have secondary conceptions and beliefs which can explain away such refutations, one at a time, provided that not all are faced together. Thus the successful countering of one obstacle strengthens the whole system. The theories of Marx and Freud (the particular objects of Popper's criticisms) operate in similar ways. But, unlike Popper, Polanyi does not hold that a clear and simple division between science and non-science can be made in this respect. For science, too, has its ways of explaining recalcitrant phenomena, and must have them, especially that of 'anomaly', since there always is some discrepant reading or result, and science would come to a halt if some were not ignored. Only totally blank minds would be liberated, by a truly universal doubt, from holding uncritical and preconceived beliefs. And such minds could not express themselves, since language can be acquired only by the a-critical assimilation of what others say and therefore of the view of the world embodied in it (e.g. a magical one in the case of Zande children, a more naturalistic in the case of modern Europeans). It would have to induce a state of non-perception, an uncomprehending experience of mere images. For, as empirical psychology has shown, in contradiction to Empiricist speculations and assumptions, seeing is not just opening one's eyes but the result of many efforts to interpret and make sense of visual images.

In Chapter 10 Polanyi faces the Objectivist objection that all this will result in a morass of subjectivism, a charge which many have levelled against *Personal Knowledge,* because they can think in no other terms than 'Objectivist' (good) and 'Subjectivist' (bad). Now Polanyi does not attempt to hide behind seemingly impersonal statements of the form, 'it is true that...'. He openly declares that it is he, Michael Polanyi, who is speaking and trying to search for his ultimate beliefs. But this is a responsible and personal endeavour — to find the truth, 'worthy of all men to be believed'. The personal is precisely the subjection of oneself to requirements and a reality beyond the self. Therein it is not subjective, and, as the effort of an individual (as it must be) it is not objective either, but beyond that vicious dichotomy. This responsible self-subjection is what Polanyi calls 'commitment', whereas the subjective is a condition to which the person is subject. The personal is a self-dedication to universal standards which can be said to be known, not impersonally as mere facts, but as binding upon oneself. 'You cannot speak without self-contradiction of knowledge you do not believe, or of a reality which does not exist', and so commitment, 'in this sense is the only path for approaching the universally valid' (*PK* p.303).

Polanyi proceeds to draw an important distinction between beliefs seen from within a situation of commitment and the same seen from without. The switch from the former to the latter reduces the beliefs to mere facts about the person holding them and not to confident utterances about reality. Their contents become 'alleged facts' rather than facts themselves. The personal engagement and commitment of the subject then becomes mere subjectivity. There are many examples of this in some deliberately debunking works of sociology and psychology, wherein the supposedly impartial and detached observer, *because of his very detachment,* does not endorse any of the beliefs and practices he is studying. He puts them all into quotation marks and so turns them into mere beliefs, mere facts about the believer and not about the world. And also by this detachment he discredits, by ignoring, any responsible endeavour of his subjects to find and believe what is true, although they may be mistaken. We see this in the effects, and sometimes in the intentions, of the sociology of knowledge — the sceptical

Relativism which arises whenever people's beliefs are treated as mere facts.

When the debunking mind which cannot accept commitment turns on itself, it is torn, as Hume showed in his case, between 'a demand for impersonality which would discredit all commitment and an urge to make up his mind which drives him to recommit himself'. Polanyi takes the correspondence theory of truth (that a statement is true if it corresponds to the facts) more as an account of how to arrive at truth rather than as a definition of truth. He then argues that the alignment of one's subjective beliefs with the facts, which the theory requires when thus interpreted, would be impossible. For one can speak of the 'actual facts' only by believing them, by viewing them from within commitment. Otherwise they are 'alleged facts'. Conversely, by speaking of one's 'subjective beliefs' one has stepped outside commitment and now regards one's beliefs as mere facts, mere states of mind. But *'truth is something that can be thought of only by believing it'* (*PK* p.305).

The difference between the personal and the merely subjective lies in the sense of responsibility shown in the former and the lack of responsibility (i.e. surrender to irresponsibility or being overcome by some compulsion or neurotic obsession) in the latter. We act responsibly when we strive to fulfil universal standards, for example, in seeking what is true or what is just. This is the Lutheran freedom of 'Here I stand and can do no other', in contrast to the irresponsible freedom of doing and thinking what one likes. The effort to fulfil a universal standard narrows one's choice until one finds the one thing that is to be done. *'The freedom of the subjective person to do as he pleases is overruled by the freedom of the responsible person to act as he must'* (*PK* p.309).

Responsible commitment seeks a reality which is independent of our knowing it, and thus is more than what we know of it. All new knowledge, argues Polanyi, is like Columbus' discovery of America — a fragment of what turns out to be a far greater whole. Reality shows itself in this way: that there proves to be more than we first apprehend and than what we can anticipate. Were what is real only a product of our minds, then it would not have unforeseen dimensions. (Hence fictional characters who come alive on the page outrun their creators' initial thoughts of them, and appear more to be discoveries than inventions.) But what is sought can be missed, and every discovery has to go beyond what is already known. It is a venture into unknown territory, and its success cannot be guaranteed in advance. Knowing and discovery are things which we do, and not passive experiences which we merely suffer or enjoy. As activities, they aim at achievements (i.e. what is true and real) and so there is an inherent risk of failure.

> To believe something is a mental act: you can neither believe nor disbelieve a passive experience. It follows that you can only believe something which might be false. This is my argument in a nutshell (*PK* p.313).

Polanyi expands this by citing the processes of a child's development, as it comes to separate itself from the world and other people, and to acquire a distinction between fact and fiction. Thereby it incurs the possibility of error. In infancy perception takes place automatically; eventually, however, there emerges the conscious self, which has to choose deliberately between alternative interpretations of what it sees, as with a picture that can be seen as either a vase or two faces. To choose neither is not to see anything. And we cannot postpone choices until we have had more time to consider the evidence. For to do that is itself a choice between the risks of being hasty and those of further hesitation. Always to hesitate would end in stupor, which eliminates not only error but also belief and therefore knowledge. Thus a consistent scepticism could not express itself. To do so, it would have to use language, which is learned by induction from others' usage and therefore liable to be mislearned and to incorporate errors. It is in this way, Polanyi concludes, that is resolved the paradox of our observance of standards which we set for ourselves. In so doing, we perform competent mental acts, and therefore we do not do as we please but we force ourselves to act as we must.

Objectivism seeks to evade commitment by means of the devices which we have already noted: *viz.* the pseudo-substitutions for truth and reality. Another device is to argue that since scientific theories have been disproved in the past, they are now held only as hypotheses and not as true. But they are certainly not held to be *false*, and, because our beliefs change, it does not follow that we are not holding them, are not holding them to be true, and so are not committed to them. It is a fallacy to argue 'that we are never committed because our commitments are changing' (*PK* p.308).

In opposition to Objectivist attempts to avoid the inevitability of commitment, Polanyi urges that we accept our calling to use the limited and fallible means that we are born with, the conditions in which we grow up, and the cultural forms which we inherit, so as to try to achieve the universal obligations to which we are subject. (This appeal is similar to Ricoeur's for acceptance and for an ethics of risk and daring — *Freedom and Nature*, Pt III, Chap. III.) Objectivism, seeking to 'relieve us from all responsibility for the holding our beliefs' (*PK* p.323), results in the elimination of human responsibility. This can be seen in the vision of Laplace, wherein the whole future of the universe can be computed from a knowledge of the initial position and velocities of its atoms and the laws governing their movements; it can be seen, too, in Behaviourist and Freudian psychology; in Marxist economic determinism; and in the socio-biology of E.O. Wilson. But liberation from Objectivism does not mean that we gain the nihilistic freedom which permits us to do as we please. We escape from Objectivism only in our efforts to fulfil our calling and so to re-affirm our responsibility. We consciously take upon ourselves the hopes, commitments and service of standards which heretofore we have implicitly held and practised.

Polanyi is engaged in a process of self-discovery in which he invites his readers to join. He is in search of those ultimate beliefs which we cannot but hold while we live and think, whether we realise it or not and whether we would explicitly acknowledge them or not. He attempts, in effect, to show that the Objectivist does not, and cannot, really believe in or act upon Objectivism; for his everyday actions, and the science which he accepts, presuppose a very different set of beliefs. Polanyi's argument is a presuppositional one: that such-and-such are beliefs presupposed in every moment of our waking and thinking life. Such an argument starts with central and pervasive features of human life, such as language or the use of our sensory-motor system, and seeks to reveal what we implicitly believe by using and trusting in them. Polanyi's approach is therefore akin to, but wider than, Collingwood's conception of metaphysics (in *An Essay on Metaphysics*) as the formulation of 'absolute presuppositions'.

Now both approaches contradict the assumptions and procedures of 'justificatory', 'critical' and 'foundational' philosophy. The last regards what we ordinarily believe, or what science claims to have discovered, as in some way defective, and thus in need of 'justification', 'criticism' and 'founding'. Acording to this view, the task of philosophy is to supply what is lacking, and so to turn our unwarranted beliefs into genuine knowledge, by showing how they are derived from, or underwritten by, indubitable first principles (Descartes), or from simple 'ideas', 'impressions' or 'sense-data' (the Empiricists from Locke to Russell), or from a manifold of sensations upon which we impose a set of schemata and concepts so as to make it into the representation of a coherent world (Kant). Sooner or later all such attempts are found to be wanting and the result is that we are left without any knowledge at all. But this Scepticism cannot be lived, nor can it express itself. Polanyi therefore seeks to formulate and practise a 'post-critical philosophy' which starts with our implicit trust in our everyday beliefs and practices, and which draws out from them the higher beliefs and practices which they presuppose. Only such a procedure, he claims, is self-consistent. For the 'critical' philosopher, in his attempts to 'justify' by critical scrutiny, has to use, trust and so implicitly believe in the very things he claims to be doubting, testing and justifying — his powers of perception, induction and other forms of inference, learning and use of language, and so on. Not only can the critical attitude not be lived, but neither can it be practised in philosophy.

As Polanyi several times points out, it is our ordinary beliefs, in daily life and in science, which are primary and the more certain. Whatever is formulated from them is secondary and dependent upon them. This is the reverse of 'critical' and 'justificatory' assumptions. Thus any premisses of science which we may formulate are found by reflection upon the way we have already established facts, and are not known prior to scientific investigations and the establishment of facts. We believe in explicit presuppositions only because we have discovered them in facts which we already believe. We have to acknowledge authentic instances of science and scientific truths, law, music, historical facts, and the like, before we can try to formulate the premisses and presuppositions of those activities (*PK* pp.162-3). Normally we know such things only implicitly in and through the practice of the relevant activity. That is why, explains Polanyi, the practitioners of an activity can accept and re-iterate a false formulation of its premisses and presuppositions — such as Positivist and Objectivist accounts of science — because they tacitly correct the explicit formulation in accordance with their implicit knowledge of its genuine premisses and presuppositions. Likewise any explicit formulation of scientific method is bound to be ambiguous, and will be automatically supplemented by the scientist's tacit knowledge of the procedures which he implicitly follows. And the rules formulated by philosophers are not, nor can be, used to resolve any genuine problem because, as explicit formulations, they are ambiguous and incomplete (*PK* pp.169-70).

Polanyi's presuppositional approach can accredit itself, and is the only one that can do so. Is it, then, merely a circular argument? In one way, it is and cannot be otherwise. As we noted above, we can state our ultimate beliefs only from within our convictions. Self-consistency is the ultimate court of appeal. But that is also consistency with the conditions in which we speak: *viz.* our existence as embodied intelligences in the world. A successful articulation of ultimate beliefs will issue in the explication of those beliefs which, as intelligent beings in the world, we cannot but hold while we live and think. And that is their only 'justification'. In this way Polanyi differs from Rorty (in *Philosophy and the Mirror of Nature*) who also rejects 'foundational' philosophy but who can find nothing else for philosophy to do but to oscillate between a mistaken 'foundational' approach and an 'edifying' one which merely criticises it.

But it does not follow from this that we are trapped within any less than ultimate framework of thought. This is what Polanyi's theory of tacit knowing can explain, whereas no view which regards all knowledge as explicit can show how it is possible to go beyond what we already hold to be true. We not only indwell our intellectual framework; because we tacitly control what we explicitly believe, we can break out of them. Because we tacitly hold our beliefs to be true, we can correct them as we begin to grope towards a different view of things. It is this tacit direction of our beliefs beyond themselves to the world, which, anchoring our commitments, enables us to amend them. But, if knowing were knowing that we know, there would be nothing beyond what we explicitly know whereby we could correct it. Here then we have an ultimate commitment: that beyond all the particular things that we claim to know, there is a real world to which they are directed.

Only an acknowledgment of our power to know more than we can tell can account for the fact of discovery, and thus also for the possibility of breaking out of one system of thought and taking on, or building up, a new one. Here Polanyi refers to the ancient problem set forth in Plato's *Meno*: How can one discover something, since either one knows what one is looking for, and so knows it already, or one does not and so cannot recognise it when one meets it? Plato's own answer, that learning is really remembering what we have already seen in a previous life, has not been accepted (nor does it explain how we could learn anything in that previous life). Yet none other has been offered; for two thousand years men have been familiar with discovery and have made thousands of important discoveries; but they have never been able to say how they do it. It has been either pointless or impossible. Now what makes discovery possible is our ability to switch our attention, so that, instead of attending to what we already know, we begin to try to attend *from* it and *to* what it indicates or means. That is, we now use it as a set of clues to something which is as yet only dimly sensed by us as a new coherence or meaning of these particular facts. As such, the hidden reality is not yet focally known to us. Either it spontaneously appears to us, like the sudden seeing of a hidden face in a puzzle picture, or we strive to bring it into focus and to see it for what it is. In either case, we discover what we did not previously know by using items of our present knowledge as clues and thus by attending from them. And therefore the hidden reality can be recognised, since it is the meaning (the semantic aspect) of those particular details which we use as clues to it. If all knowledge were explicit and lacked the from-to structure of tacit integration, then we could never discover anything, nor recognise something new (*TD* pp.23-6).

This in turn means that the world itself is structured by a from-to integration of details into significant wholes or patterns. That there is a real world, independent of our knowing it, is not all that the philosophy of tacit integration can say about the world. And to the ontological and cosmological dimensions of Polanyi's philosophy we now turn.

5. COMPREHENSIVE ENTITIES AND COMPLEX PERFORMANCES

Polanyi returns time and again to the argument, directed against the Positivist elements in Objectivism, that real things show themselves in ways which we cannot anticipate. In that way, we may add, we often tell more than we can know. A theory that is true will thus have unforeseen consequences which themselves are true, and of which most are to be discovered empirically but some perhaps, Polanyi insists, by theoretical deduction. Reality is more than we know at any moment, and will show itself to be so. It follows from this, he argues, that an entity which reveals itself in more ways than another is therefore more real. Persons and problems are more profound and therefore more real than cobblestones, though the latter are more tangible (*TD* pp. 32-3). In this way Polanyi reinstates the ancient conception of degrees of reality and does so in a direction contrary to that of Reductionism, which assumes the more tangible to be the more real.

Problems, or acts of solving them, and persons are examples, respectively, of what Polanyi calls complex performances and comprehensive entities. These have an ontological structure parallel to our knowledge of them. For in knowing them we attend to them and from their subsidiary details as well as from clues in ourselves (such as the two slightly different retinal images that give us stereoscopic vision), and from clues in the context joining us and them (such as an object's possession of a definite outline which sets it off against its background). It is here that we enter the realms of life, mind and the works of mind. And it is here that Polanyi argues the case against the Reductionist tendencies of Objectivism.

Let us return to the *ontological* aspect of tacit integration. A comprehensive entity, or complex performance, exists on at least two levels: that of its subsidiary details and that of the entity or performance itself into which they are organised. Polanyi gives the example of making a speech. That involves the five levels of producing sounds, words, sentences, style and composition. Each level is governed by its own laws, respectively, phonetics, lexicography, grammar, stylistics and literary criticism. Each level is controlled by both its own laws and by those of the next level above. Thus the sounds we utter are governed by both the physiology of the human voice plus those of the vocabulary of the language which we speak; the words are chosen for their meanings but are ordered, and inflected, according to the rules of grammar; and the sentences thus emerging are ordered by a sense of style, itself chosen as appropriate to the type of speech being made. This is the system of *dual control*. On each level its own laws or operational principles leave open the limits within which they operate — the *boundary conditions* of that level. Thus the range of sounds which the human voice can produce leaves open the ones which are to be used by a given language (German is gutteral; Portuguese is full of 's', 'sh' and 'z' sounds), and the strength, flexibility and endurance of each metal leaves open just which metal, within these limits, can be successfully used for a particular part in a given type of machine. This determination of the boundary conditions of one level by the operational principles of the next highest level, is called *the principle of marginal control* (*TD* pp. 34-40, *SOM* Lect. 2).

To perceive or understand a comprehensive entity or complex performance we have to attend from its lower levels to the highest one. Thus in watching a game of chess we shall not understand what is going on if we pay attention only to the physical movements of the pieces. For that would be to ignore the meaning of the pieces and the movements — 'Q to KB4' — just as by listening to the word it becomes only a sound to us and we lose its meaning. Nor is it enough to attend to the rules. For they determine only the moves that can be made. They can tell us that 'Q to KB4' is legitimate or not. But to understand that move we have to look to the situation on the board and to the player's strategy. If he has no strategy, then the move is incomprehensible. Again, merely by looking at a collection of pieces of metal we cannot grasp what machine they compose. To do that we must look *from* them and *to* the function of the whole and of each set of parts within it. And this is what we in fact do — we attend *from* the move itself to what we take to be the player's aim, and *from* the pieces *to* their presumed functions and the function of the whole. Not to do so is to destroy, or not to find, the meaning of the move or the part, and so not to see the game or the machine, but only a series of unrelated and incomprehensible moves or a collection of unrelated and incomprehensible parts.

Now Reductionism is the claim that a higher level has no reality or operational principles of its own, and thus that it can be entirely explained by reference to the particulars of a lower level and its laws. Objectivism, preferring what is measurable and apparently impersonal, therefore hopes to explain everything else — living organisms and their life-processes, persons and their actions, machines and their functions — by reference to the physical particulars out of which they are composed, and thus by the laws of physics and chemistry which apply to physical particulars. Thus the intelligent actions of people are to be explained in terms of conditioned reflexes, of unconscious desires and fears, or of their membership of a given social class, and so Behaviourist or Freudian psychology, or Marxist or neo-Marxist sociology, will replace biography and history. In turn these events will be explained by the organic structure and functioning of the human body, and thus physiology and biology will replace psychology and sociology. Finally, for the most thorough-going Reductionists, organic functions and processes will be explained by reference to the chemical and physical laws governing molecules and atoms. The end result is Laplace's vision, Polanyi's favourite example of full-blooded Objectivism, in which everything can be understood by reference to the initial positions and velocities of atoms and the laws governing their movements.

But these successive reductions cannot be carried out. Let us take the example of Behaviourist psychology — whether that of Watson,

Skinner or Ryle — which claims to understand the operations of people's minds in terms of their manifest behaviour. Polanyi cites Ryle's contention that 'Overt intelligent performances are not clues to the workings of minds; they are those workings' (e.g. *PK* p. 372). But if we simply observe what people do, then we lose the sense of their actions. For example, we observe A and B running along the street. What is happening here? A race? A chase? Both men after the same thing? Or two unrelated events? Merely by attending *to* their specific movements — such as A turning round, B taking the same path as A — we shall not understand what is happening. We have to attend *from* these particular events and try to bring into focus the whole action — that is, to try to see what A and B are each *trying* to do, the pattern into which each is fitting his particular actions. That is, in turn, to attend *with* A and B to their aims and objectives, and, as they organise their movements into the complex perform- ance (whatever it is), to reconstruct it with or after them. They go from the whole (to catch the bus, to be first at the finishing line, to outwit B or to catch A) to the parts (to accelerate as the bus appears to be nearer than first thought, to keep within catching distance of the leaders, to turn aside when B cannot see it or to shorten the distance by cutting the corner more obliquely than did A), whereas we go from the parts to the whole and then see, if we have got it right, the other parts intelligible in its light. We indwell their movements as they primarily indwell them. Indeed, we are largely ignorant of the details, in themselves, of our own and others' bodily movements and appearances, and are aware of them only subsidiarily and tacitly as we attend from them and to our, or their, thoughts, intentions and actions. The mind is therefore the meaning of the body. (See further 'The Structure of Consciousness' in *KB*.)

What Reductionists in fact do is to offer only pseudo-substitutions for that level of reality, and its principles, which they claim to explain away. They trade on their implicit grasp of that level in offering purported substitutes for it. Thus Ryle, confusing meaning of with evidence for, offered lists of typical actions which, he claimed, are attitudes or emotions. But he relied upon a tacit grasp of the latter for selecting the items in his lists. Similarly one who claims that machines or organisms can be explained by the physics and chemistry of their component atoms and molecules, has first to identify, on the basis of his everyday practical knowledge, a machine and its purpose or an organism and its functions, before he can then begin to analyse its subsidiary details in themselves. What a study of its lower levels can provide is a knowledge of the limits within which it operates or lives, and of how it can break down, go wrong, become ill or die. By being embodied in matter, the operational principles of machines, the functioning of organisms, and the thoughts and actions of minds, are put at risk by the lower levels on which they depend. Thus once a computer, its programme and the functions of its parts have been identified as such, and once from such knowledge we recognize that it is malfunctioning or not working at all, then a knowledge of physics and chemistry can tell us just how it has broken down — just what over-load of current has blown a fuse, or at what temperature a joint has become unsoldered or a piece of plastic has melted, and just how this prevents the computer from working. But no knowledge of the materials in themselves can identify a computer, *just* as a knowledge of the shapes of a script cannot by itself decipher it.

Moreover, higher levels are not merely bound by the lower on which they depend, but, sometimes at least, they can use other means instead. Thus Polanyi quotes examples of equipotentiality from biology, such as rats being able still to run a maze even though the neural paths used in learning it have been cut (*PK* p. 339). Even more so can persons show originality and extend their physical and mental powers. Thus the activity of speech and the use of our fingers not only take advantage of the human larynx and fingers, but, even in the short course of human evolution, have extended the physical powers of larynx and fingers. And human ingenuity has enabled us to perceive and make things beyond our unaided perceptual and physical powers. None of these original achievements, in uses of alternative means and extensions of innate powers, can be explained in terms of the lower levels which are used as alternatives or extended to serve the purpose of animals and men.

It follows that biology, technology, psychology and history are successively logically richer than physics and chemistry. In the former sciences there is an essential element of the *appraisal* of the standards of the subject-matter itself. In these sciences we study *achievements*, not just events. Biology thus studies the living machinery that is organisms and their principles of operation. It evaluates organisms, their organs and their functioning as mature or immature, as true or untrue to type, as well formed or malformed, as healthy or injured or diseased, as fertile or sterile. It thus involves a much more personal indwelling of its subject-matter than do physics and chemistry: firstly because these states of organisms and their organs cannot be precisely defined, nor can the species and genera to which individuals belong; and secondly, because the biologist is not just observing and experimenting with but evaluating his subject-matter in terms of its immanent standards or rules of rightness. The same applies to the technological sciences in their identification and study of machines and other devices. Even more so in psychology, the investigator has to indwell and evaluate the achievements, or failures, of the animals and people whom he studies. Thus in the psychology of learning, he has to recognize for himself the right way to run a maze, operate a lever to obtain food, solve an equation or pick out a pattern, before he can appraise the degree of success, or failure, shown by his subjects in learning to do these things. His psychology cannot tell him these things — only his own practical, mathematical or perceptual knowledge. What psychology can do is to show how rats, apes and people set about doing these things, under what conditions they tend to succeed, and under what ones they fail (*PK* Chaps. 11-2).

It also follows, we may add, that the much-vaunted dichotomy of fact and value, description and evaluation, is erroneous, outside of the world of physics and chemistry. For in the worlds of life, machinery and mind, descriptions *are* evaluations, since the facts *are* achievements or failures. To say 'This is a computer' is to appraise it as a *working* machine which will perform *valid* operations on data fed into it; otherwise we should have to add, 'but it does not work' or 'its programming is faulty'. Again, to say that 20 out of 24 rats ran the maze after three attempts, is to say that they ran is *successfully* after three attempts. A value-free biology, psychology, technology or history is not to be had.

The increasing logical richness of the studies of life and mind can be seen in the greater complexity of standards applied in the latter. In biology there are only health or disease, correct or incorrect formation, growth and functioning. But, according to Polanyi, in the study of animal and human intelligence there are four basic possibilities:
1. correct satisfaction of normal standards;
2. mistaken satisfaction of normal standards;
3. action or perception satisfying subjective, illusory standards;
4. mental derangement issuing in meaningless reactions (*PK* p. 363).

From this list Polanyi has omitted the parallel to (2): the mistaken satisfaction of illusory standards. For in (1) and (2) we endorse the standards employed by the animal or person under investigation, say, in obtaining food from the other side of a cage or in solving a logical problem, and judge his results as correct or incorrect in their light. But in (3) we judge his standards themselves to be mistaken, as when an animal uses a totally inappropriate method for obtaining food or a person indulges in sheer guessing to solve a problem. In such a case, the result can be either successful (by chance) or unsuccessful. In (4), in contrast to all the foregoing, there is no intelligent activity but blind and totally random behaviour. The point is that in the study of animal and human intelligence there are two levels of evaluation: of the particular action and its results; and of the standards employed therein, or of their absence (possibility No. (4)).

In biology the investigator stands over his subject-matter and evaluates it in terms of its own principles of rightness. But in psychology he stands alongside his subject-matter, for the principles of rightness — in perception, learning, and thinking — are also his own. But when we come to history and biography, and our daily intercourse with our fellows, there are moments when we stand under those other persons in that we take from them standards and rules of rightness — for thinking, conduct, performances of arts and crafts — for these persons have superior knowledge, and some, the geniuses and heroes of mankind, set new standards for us all. At such moments we surrender ourselves to the superior person, as we do in all acts of learning from others, since we cannot judge superior standards in the light of our present and inferior ones, nor, in any case, can we judge any standards in the same way that we judge other things by means of them. The climax of the study of man comes in the study of those great men from whom we take our standards instead of applying ours to them. Of course, as with Napoleon, an historically important man can be wrongly taken as a model. None of us is infallible in anything, and a man's achievements may be very ambiguous. But there is no alternative to the acritical adaptation of oneself to the standards and judgments of some other persons (*PK* pp. 374-9, *SOM* pp. 71-960.

Polanyi, therefore, rejects the usual sharp division, made by Dilthey and most German philosophers after him, between 'explanation' in the natural sciences and 'understanding' and 'empathy' in the human ones. He gives particular attention to biology, the whole sphere of life between matter and mind, which Cartesianism, and modern thought following it, simply omits or reduces to mere matter. Biology also is a discipline of 'understanding' and assessment, and animal psychology is yet more logically complex in its orders of assessment. Thus for Polanyi there is more of a scale of studies than two radically distinct sets. This scale of increasing complexity, and of orders of appraisal and criticism, reflects the hierarchy of levels of being in the things themselves.

A world that includes comprehensive entities and complex performances is a world of levels of existence. Polanyi therefore gives attention, in the final chapter of *Personal Knowledge*, to the emergence in the course of evolution of new and higher levels — life, sentience, intelligence and man. Just as the higher levels within the particular comprehensive entity cannot be identified by, nor explained in terms of, their subsidiary details of the lower levels, so too in evolution the emergence of new and higher levels cannot be explained in terms of those previously existing. Evolution is itself an achievement: the story of the emergence of ever more complex forms of achievements. All that can be explained by reference to events of a lower level is how and when the action of evolutionary principles is released and sustained — how, as it were, opportunities occur for the emergence of living beings out of inanimate matter, or of perceptive beings out of merely animate ones. The error of Darwin's attempted explanation of the mechanism of evolution was that it merely revealed the *conditions* of evolution and ignored its *action* (*PK* pp. 382-90). It can explain only how one species turns into another, but never how living species, and then species with powers of perception, and then human intelligence, arose in the first place. (Likewise the chemistry of DNA cannot be used to explain everything in biology — see 'Life's Irreducible Structure' in *KB*.) Polanyi attempts to offer an account that presumes neither that all future developments were already but invisibly present in the primeval state of the universe, nor that they are the results of successive divine interventions. It seems to me, however, that all that Polanyi accomplishes, in these final pages of *Personal Knowledge,* is to show again that the emergence of new levels of existence cannot be accounted for in terms of lower and already existing levels.

The cosmology which Polanyi provides is thus one of a multi-level universe, in which each level has its own reality and autonomy, while depending upon those below it and being shaped by those above. Only such a cosmology, in contrast to the uni-level views resulting from Objectivism, is consistent with the claim to speak about the universe. It is one of Polanyi's persistent criticisms of Objectivism, and the specific views which it engenders, that they cannot account for themselves. For example, Laplace's claim that a knowledge of the positions and velocities of all atoms, and of the laws governing their movements, would yield a predictive knowl-

edge of the whole course of the universe, simply eliminates everything but atoms in motion and thus the scientist who is supposed to
know all this (—p. 142). Similarly reductive biologies, psycholo-
gies and sociologies discredit the originality and intelligence of
animals and men by seeking to explain them in terms of events on
lower levels. They thereby discredit themselves as achievements of
human intelligence, for they have no room for the intelligent and
disinterested search for the truth about a world independent of our
knowing it. They therefore open the way for, and offer themselves
as the instruments of, totalitarian ideologies which demand total
control by the State, because they claim that man is (in the pregnant
words taken as a title by B.F. Skinner) 'beyond freedom and
dignity'. They refuse to recognize our standards — of thought and
conduct — and so reduce us to the play of sub-human and irresponsible forces. Objectivism is not merely a pernicious intellectual
error but, more dangerously, a standing threat to the free society.

6. THE RESTORATION OF FREEDOM AND MEANING

Objectivism is a threat, in Polanyi's view, to human freedom and dignity in several ways. The Reductionist views of man which it generates explicitly remove human responsibility, as does implicitly its view of knowledge as impersonal. Its ideal of knowledge saps our convictions in undemonstrable standards and ideals of truth, justice and freedom. It thereby releases an uncontrolled will to domination and power. Thus it reinforces the Marxist and other claims, to which it gives rise, that society can be reconstructed and ruled according to an exact science.

Objectivism results not only in a scepticism towards undemonstrable standards and ideals, but also in an 'unmasking' of moral ideals and motives — as the results of self-interest, 'bourgeois prejudices', as the ideological projections of one's social class, as conditioned reflexes, as repression of instinctive forces, as a 'will to power' or *ressentiment*. But, while such unmasking and debunking operate explicitly, those who engage in them implicitly congratulate themselves on their moral superiority in being free of such illusions. Hence arises the 'honesty' of that naked force and unscrupulousness, which does not shelter behind the 'hypocritical' appeals to the ideals and moral sentiments which Objectivist assumptions expose as unfounded. Whereas Machiavelli would have allowed a disregard of moral considerations in the name of expediency, modern totalitarians can openly proclaim a resolve to act unscrupulously, while implicitly claiming credit for their 'honesty'. Polanyi cites, as examples of this outlook, the advocates of *Realpolitik* in Imperial Germany who stated that Might was Right, Hitler in his appeals to German youth, and Marxism.

The deadly combination of explicit Objectivism, in denying standards and ideals, with implicit moral passion, is what Polanyi calls a 'dynamo-objective coupling'. It combines the dynamism which the modern world has inherited from the Christian hope of perfection (which it secularises and wants to see realized here on earth) with the destructive forces of Objectivist assumptions. In Marxism, the clearest and most potent example, the negative side is formed by the Objectivist unmasking of all moral ideals as 'bourgeois ideology' and 'ideological superstructures', set up to legitimate the capitalist exploitation of the proletariat. And the positive and dynamic side is the desire for a classless Utopia here on earth in which there will be no exploitation. But, because of Marx's Objectivist assumptions, this cannot be explicitly upheld as a *moral* ideal and imperative. It must therefore be disguised in objective terms, as the inevitable result of a mechanical but 'dialectical' process which can be 'scientifically' demonstrated to be at work in history. Hence Marx's claim that his socialism was science and not Utopia. Thus emerges a 'dynamo-objective' coupling, wherein an implicit moral desire for perfection is explicitly denied by Objectivist beliefs, and at the same time is disguised in 'objective' statements, the result being an unashamed and open lack of scruple.

This, argues Polanyi, explains the appeal of an ideology such as Marxism to men like Sartre, Picasso and Bernal, whose intellectual pursuits Marxism declares to be a part of 'bourgeois ideology', and which it would subordinate to the Party and the State. For Marxism 'enables the modern mind, tortured by moral self-doubt, to indulge its moral passions in terms which also satisfy its passion for ruthless objectivity' (*PK* p. 228). Indeed, the negative side of Marxism increases the intellectual's insecurity and the positive side thereupon offers him a haven and an 'objective' meaning to his existence and a task for him. Generally, argues Polanyi (e.g. in 'Beyond Nihilism' in *KB*), individual nihilism — the contemptuous rejection of all standards and ideals, especially traditional ones — as represented by Turgenev's Bazarov and Dostoyevsky's Raskolnikov, has been superseded by the more dynamic, political and organized nihilism of the totalitarian movements. Sartrean Existentialism, making life and the individual meaningless, is thus tempted by Marxist ideology, which offers a meaning and purpose to life while at the same time endorsing the nihilist's disgust with 'bourgeois society'.

Against this Polanyi supports an essentially limited politics. He argues for the necessity of accepting an admittedly imperfect society and set of institutions, just as generally we have to accept our calling within our situations and all their limitations:

> An absolute moral renewal of society can be attempted only by an absolute power which must inevitably destroy the moral life of man.... The attempt made in this book to stabilize knowledge against scepticism, by including its hazardous character in the conditions of knowledge, may find its equivalent, then, in an allegiance to a manifestly imperfect society, based on the acknowledgement that our duty lies in the service of ideals which we cannot possibly achieve (*PK* p. 245).

Yet, much as he admired and enjoyed the Anglo-American traditions of civic liberty, he found Anglo-American Liberalism — the tradition of Locke, Hume, Bentham and the Mills — to be seriously at fault. For that also stems from the same premisses as the nihilism which leads to revolutionary terror and totalitarian ideology. (Recall J.S. Mill's repeated defence of freedom of speech on the grounds that no one *knows* what is true.) In Britain and America those ideas were tamed and supplemented by the living tradition of continuing institutions, which were more than the theorists could tell. But as a Hungarian, brought up in an atmosphere of radical free-thought and having experienced at first hand both revolution and counter-revolution, Polanyi knew that elsewhere people do draw the logical consequences of their beliefs, and are prepared to act upon them, rather than to shut them away as did Hume with his moral scepticism. Hence Polanyi argues that we must go 'beyond nihilism' and recover an acknowledgement and devotion to truth, while fully recognising that it cannot be demonstrated.

Hence he saw hope in the liberation from ideology achieved by those prominent in the Hungarian revolution of 1956, and by others

who similarly came to see through the deceptions of Marxism, sym-
bolised most poignantly by the faked trials where all — judges and
the accused themselves — accepted lies at the behest of the Party
('The Message of the Hungarian Revolution' in *KB*.)

But the Objectivist domination of thought is not confined to the
states under Marxist rule. Indeed, it dominates much of British and
American academic life, in the form of the various Reductionisms.
Hence the refusal of some scholars in free countries to recognize the
true message of the Hungarian revolution. Instead of seeing its
significance and causes in the recovery of a sense of, and respect for,
truth, and a rejection of a false and degrading ideology, such scholars
tried to explain it (in semi-Marxist terms) as a consequence of
changed social conditions, especially industrialisation. (Similar
explanations have been given of current reforms in the Soviet
Union.) Polanyi quotes the historian, Professor R. Pipes, who
confessed to suppressing a statement that the Russian intellectuals'
task was 'to fight for truth', since it sounded 'naive and unscientific'
(*KB* p. 26).

Polanyi draws two morals from attitudes such as this: that 'value-
free' social and political science, limiting itself to description, and
forgoing evaluation, undermines the free society and its institutions,
by turning all moral and political commitments into mere facts about
people's beliefs; and that in doing this it is not neutral and 'value-
free' as it claims, and indeed that no 'value-free' study of man is
possible. 'Value-free' social science in effect denies that there is
successful or mistaken satisfaction of normal standards, and so it
turns all standards into subjective and illusory ones. Indeed, in the
terms of the possibilities which we noted in the previous chapter, it
makes all moral and political conduct, indeed all conduct whatso-
ever, compulsive and irrational. For in making moral judgments, as
all men in fact do even though some deny it, we refer to moral
standards which we hold to be universally valid, to be *right* and not
just matters of personal taste. That entails a distinction between
moral truth and *moral illusion*, and, in turn, one between being
motivated by moral truth, which is founded on claims that can be

supported by evidence and argument, and between being compulsively moved by moral illusions just as we are by perceptual illusions. Thus, once we admit that there are valid moral judgments and genuine values, then '*we have implicitly denied the claim that all human actions can be explained without reference to the exercise of moral judgment*' (*KB* p. 33). Thus the Hungarians to whom Polanyi refers, revolted against faked trials because they *believed* them to be wrong. If there really are moral values and standards, then they may have been rebelling against a real evil, and because they knew it to be evil, not because they were compelled by economic necessity or propaganda or some other cause. But to decide which of these motives is in operation, we first have to establish whether there are genuine values — e.g. whether faked trials are truly evil. Such judgments are therefore necessary to the political scientist's explanation of people's conduct (*KB* pp. 33-4).

Polanyi therefore rejects Ricker's and Weber's claim that the human sciences can recognize actions which can be praised or blamed but must themselves desist from praise and blame. We may generalize Polanyi's argument to all human studies. Thus if no genuine literary values exist, Shakespeare was as deluded about his poetry as William McGonegall was clearly deluded about his, and was just as much (or just as little) a fraud as any Grub Street hack or student plagiarist.

This, then, is Polanyi's general argument: that a free society needs a commitment by its members to truth and a mutual respect for each other's self-dedication. Conversely, truth can be pursued only in a free society, where intellectual pursuits are nourished and sustained by that general dedication which allows each to develop in its appropriate way. Both sides of that equation are threatened by Objectivism and its offspring.

Polanyi distinguishes, in this respect, three forms of society:
1. static and authoritarian societies which uphold and enforce some specific beliefs, but thereby recognize the existence and importance of truth;
2. dynamic and free societies which likewise acknowledge the

existence and importance of truth, but which enforce no specific beliefs and allow freedom to all responsibly to pursue and live by truth;

3.   revolutionary and totalitarian societies, wherein the State subordinates truth to welfare (or some other aim), and assumes a monopoly of power in an attempt wholly to reshape society in accordance with its revolutionary purpose.

Types (2) and (3) are typical of the modern age, whose tragedy it is to have betrayed the hopes of the Enlightenment, because of Objectivist assumptions, and so to have moved too often from (1) to (3) rather than from (1) to (2).

Polanyi finds a model for a dynamic and free society in the 'republic of science' (see the essay of that title in *KB*). That republic is ruled by authority — as in the refereeing of papers and the awarding of degrees, grants, posts, promotions. But it is a General Authority which upholds only the standards of scientific work and the current consensus of scientific beliefs, as they have emerged so far from individual efforts which have gained general assent. It is not a Specific Authority which upholds a particular set of beliefs and theories. Furthermore, since scientific methods cannot be specified and applied in a casuistry of explicit rules, the republic of science is a community based upon tradition — the personal and tacit transmission of the unspecifiable art of scientific research and of respect for scientific truth and standards. It is thus a community of dedication — of the self-dedication of each scientist to the truth — and not of imposed servitude. Now, while fully acknowledging that the wider and inclusive community requires coercive power — the State — for its maintenance, Polanyi sees in scientific dedication a *tertium quid* both to the static imposition of specific beliefs and to the totalitarian servitude to a revolutionary ideology. A dynamic and free society requires from its citizens something like that self-dedication to the truth which constitutes the republic of science. Thereby its reforms will be gradual and cumulative and it will eschew Utopian perfectionism. It will be 'a society of explorers' wherein each sphere of life, with its own institutions and traditions, cultivates and extends its domain of truth and value, within a framework of mutual respect of each for all. Furthermore, while being dynamic and progressive, it will also be based upon and respect that tradition which is the necessary for the transmission of the tacit and personal dimensions of all knowledge. The Radicalism of Tom Paine will be tempered and restrained by the Conservatism of Edmund Burke.

Yet, one may wonder, can an actual society arise and be maintained by belief in and dedication to only formal and general principles? The republic of science exists within a wider society, or across several such societies, and participation in it is voluntary and does not occupy the whole of one's life. And so it may not be quite so apt a model for that wider society. This wider society may need to be formed upon and cohere around a more specific set of beliefs and the way of life embodying them. If so, then its continued existence depends upon upholding these specific beliefs and practices of a community, and thus it will be more like, and perhaps overlap with, a religious body, with its core of dogmas, rites and practices, than like a republic of science.

This brings us to Polanyi's effort to restore meaning to human life and the world by removing Objectivist obstacles to religious and specifically Christian beliefs. God exists, argues Polanyi (*PK* pp. 279-86), not as a fact to be observed but as someone to be worshipped and obeyed. 'God exists' is thus not a detached statement of a fact but an act of affirmation, and more like '"Snow is white" is true' than 'Snow is white'. Religious utterances are a part, with ritual, of the search for God, rather than sets of statements true, or false, in themselves. And doubt, sin and anguish are essential parts of the Christian life, and prevent it from lapsing into complacency and emptiness. The task of theology (parallel to Polanyi's conception of philosophy) is to articulate, and thence to purify, the implications of worship, but not to try to prove God's existence, which would be like trying to prove the axioms of mathematics or the premisses of induction. But while natural and historical facts cannot prove Christian belief, the refutation of those facts of which

Christian theology articulates the supernatural meaning, would undermine Christian belief. For events which did not happen cannot have any supernatural aspect. Polanyi thinks that Christianity has been purified by at least some of the scientific and historical criticisms levelled at it in and since the Enlightenment, for they have forced it to renew the grounds of Christian belief — that is, as an axiomatisation of the Christian life.

But Polanyi thinks of Christian belief only in terms of this present life. He omits entirely the hope of seeing God after this life, and thus of achieving perfection through God's grace and in eternity. Hence he wrongly asserts that Christianity holds its ideals to be unachievable as such, and sin and doubt to be of the essence of the Christian life. If we cannot achieve perfection in this life, must we not either give it up entirely or look beyond this world to the one to come? Did Polanyi sufficiently overcome the errors and dangers of the Enlightenment's secularisation of Christianity, and succeed in reconciling modern man to the limitations of his earthly existence?

Let us close with a passage wherein Polanyi summarises his case against the destructive influence of Objectivism. Man, he tells us, is

> strong, noble and wonderful so long as he fears the voices of this firmament [of values and obligations]; but he dissolves their power over himself and his own powers gained through obeying them, if he turns back and examines what he respects in a detached manner. Then law is no more than what the courts will decide, art but an emollient of nerves, morality but a convention, tradition but an inertia, God but a psychological necessity. Then man dominates a world in which he does not exist. For with his obligations he has lost his voice and his hope, and been left behind meaningless to himself (*PK* p. 380).

7. CONTINUATIONS OF POLANYI'S WORK

As I stated at the beginning, more interest in Polanyi has been shown in America than in Britain. Thus, except for *Personal Knowledge* only the American editions of his books are in print and Polanyi's papers are held by the library of the University of Chicago.

In the USA there exists a Polanyi Society, which used to be called 'The Society of Explorers', a reference to the third lecture in *The Tacit Dimension*, but which the public understood somewhat differently. The Polanyi Society publishes a journal, *Tradition and Discovery*, with which has now been merged its British equivalent, *Convivium*. From *Tradition and Discovery* can be obtained up-to-date bibliographies of publications and dissertations on Polanyi.

One of the leading figures in the Polanyi Society is Prof. Richard Gelwick, whose *The Way of Discovery* is a good introduction to Polanyi's thought, emphasising Polanyi's discovery of discovery itself and its importance in human life. Its last chapter gives details of those who have continued Polanyi's thought. Two other introductions to Polanyi are Lady Drusilla Scott's *Everyman Revived* and Prof. H. Prosch's *Michael Polanyi: A Critical Exposition*.

The chief of those who have continued Polanyi's work is undoubtedly Polanyi's collaborator, Dr Margorie Grene. Her most specifically Polanyian publication is her *The Knower and the Known*, which develops Polanyi's work in providing a post-Cartesian and post-critical form of philosophy. She edited *Knowing and Being*, a collection of Polanyi's later essays. She has also edited *The Anatomy of Knowledge*, a collection of essays by various authors in criticism of the Reductionism in much of modern science and scholarship, and *Interpretations of Life and Mind*, dedicated to Polanyi. She has been particularly interested, as was Polanyi, in biology as the neglected domain between the physical and the human sciences, as can be seen in her *Approaches to a Philosophical Biology.*

Intellect and Hope, edited by T.A. Langford and W.H. Poteat, is subtitled 'Essays in the Thought of Michael Polanyi', and contains some very interesting comparisons of Polanyi with Sartre (by Dr Grene), Wittgenstein (C.B. Daly), pre-Cartesian philosophy (E. Pols and Helmut Kuhn), J.L. Austin (Ian Ramsey) and Max Weber (Raymond Aron), together with essays in Polanyi's interpretation of science (Chaim Perelman), Polanyi and Natural Law (C.J. Friedrich), and on how Polanyi's ideas apply to the physics of clouds (W. Scott) and in biology (Sir Fancis Walshe). The editors provide an introductory essay on the problems of reading *Personal Knowledge.*

Poteat, in his *Polanyian Meditations,* has followed Polanyi's efforts to construct a post-critical philosophy.

We turn now to more specific continuations of Polanyi's work. Firstly, in theology there is *Belief in Science and in Christian Life,* edited by Prof. Thomas Torrance, which applies Polanyi's thought to theological issues, but more in the manner of Polanyi himself in the opening of theology and religion as against Objectivist dismissals of them, rather than in the manner of using his philosophy of tacit integration in the articulation of Christian doctrine itself. Prof. Torrance's *Theological Science* and other works such as *The Christian Frame of Mind,* also appeal to Polanyi's account of natural science as offering a way out of the dead-ends of Objectivisim, as does Prof. A. Peacocke's *Science and the Christian Experiment.* Prof. C. Gunton, in his *Yesterday and Today: A Study of Continuities in Christology* and *Enlightenment and Alienation,* uses Polanyi's epistemology as a framework for theology.

Another theological study of Polanyi is Fr T. Kennedy's, *The Morality of Knowledge,* while my own PhD thesis explores the problems of applying Polanyi's epistemology and ontology of tacit integration to central Christian doctrines.

In art M.H. Pirenne's *Optics, Painting and Photography,* with a foreword by Polanyi, develops Polanyi's applications of tacit integrations to our understanding of paintings, one of the themes which we have had to omit.

Gelwick cites Carl Rogers and Abraham Maslow as two American psychologists who have used Polanyi's work in developing a non-Reductionist psychology. And J. Hall has studied connections between Polanyi and the psycho-analysis of Carl Jung.

Polanyian approaches to education have been developed by R. Hodgkin in his *Born Curious* and *Playing and Exploring*, D. Holbrook in his *Education and Philosophical Anthropology*, F.N. Dunlop in his *The Education of Feeling and Emotion*, R. Brownhill in his *Education and the Nature of Knowledge*, and myself in a series of articles in *The Journal of Philosophy and Education*.

Finally, Prof. W. Scott, formerly of the University of Nevada, is working on the official biography of Polanyi.

Full details of all these works are given in the Bibliography.

BIBLIOGRAPHY

1. BOOKS BY MICHAEL POLANYI:

Knowing and Being Routledge, 1969.
The Logic of Liberty Routledge, 1951.
Meaning University of Chicago Press, 1975.
Personal Knowledge Routledge, 1958.
The Study of Man Routledge, 1959.
Science, Faith and Society OUP 1946; 2nd ed. Chicago University Press, 1964.
The Tacit Dimension Routledge, 1966.

2. OTHER WORKS CITED

R.T. Allen 'Transcendence and Immanence in the Philosophy of Michael Polanyi and Christian Theism', PhD thesis, King's College, London, 1982, (to be published in 1991 by Rutherford House, Edinburgh).

R. Brownhill *Education and the Nature of Knowledge* Croom Helm, 1983.

R.G. Collingwood *An Essay on Metaphysics* Clarendon Press, 1940.

'Lewis Carroll' 'What the Tortoise said to Achilles', *Mind*, NS Vol. 4. 1895.

F.N. Dunlop *The Education of Feeling and Emotion* Allen and Unwin, 1984.

R. Gelwick *The Way of Discovery* OUP New York, 1977.

M. Grene (ed) *The Anatomy of Knowledge* Routledge, 1969.

M. Grene *Approaches towards a Philosophical Biology* Basic Books, 1968.

M. Grene (ed) *Interpretations of Life and Mind* Humanities Press, 1971.

M. Grene *The Knower and the Known* Faber, 1966.

C. Gunton *Enlightenment and Alienation* Marshall, Morgan and Scott, 1985.

C. Gunton *Yesterday and Today* Darton, Longman and Todd, 1983.

J. Hall *Clinical Uses of Dreams* Crane and Stretton, 1977.

J. Hall *Jungian Dream Interpretation* Inner City Books 1983.

R. Hodgkin *Born Curious* Wiley, 1976.

R. Hodgkin *Playing and Exploring* Methuen, 1985.

D. Holbrook *Education and Philosophical Anthropology* Associated Universities of America Press, 1985.

P. Ignotus 'The Hungary of Michael Polanyi', in P. Ignotus *et al., The Logic of Personal Knowledge* Routledge, 1961.

T. Kennedy *The Morality of Knowledge* Academia Alfonsiana (Rome), 1979.

T. Langford and W. Poteat (eds) *Intellect and Hope* Duke University Press, 1968.

M. Merleau-Ponty *The Phenomenology of Perception* trans. C. Smith, Routledge, 1963.

A. Peacocke *Science and the Christian Experiment* OUP, 1971.

M. Pirenne *Optics, Painting and Photography,* CUP, 1971.

K. Popper *The Logic of Scientific Discovery* Hutchinson, 1959.

K. Popper *Objective Knowledge* OUP, 1972.

W. Poteat *Polanyian Meditations* Duke University Press, 1985.

H. Prosch *Michael Polanyi: A Critical Exposition* State University of New York Press, 1986.

H. Prosch 'Polanyi's Tacit Knowing and the Classic Philosophers', *Journal of the British Society for Phenomenology,* Vol. 4, No. 3, 1973.

P. Ricoeur *Nature and Freedom* Northwestern University Press, 1966.

R. Rorty *Philosophy and the Mirror of Nature* Princeton University Press, 1979.

D. Scott *Everyman Revived* The Book Guild, 1985.

B.F. Skinner *Beyond Freedom and Dignity* Bantam Books, 1972.

T. Torrance (ed) *Belief in Science and in Christian Life* Handsel Press, 1980.

T. Torrance *The Christian Frame of Mind* Handsel Press, 1985.

T. Torrance *Theological Science* OUP, 1969.

Index of Names

Index of Subjects